Rocking Rock Bottom

AWAKENING AND BOUNCING BACK

BY COURTNEY STARCHILD

Rock Bottom

BECAME THE

Solid Foundation

ON WHICH I

Rebuilt My Life

JK ROWLING SAID THAT

For My Babes

MAY YOU GROW INTO
FINE YOUNG MEN
KNOWING THAT YOU
CAN ACHIEVE

WHATEVER

YOU SET YOUR HEARTS
AND MINDS TO
I LOVE YOU MORE
THAN YOU COULD
EVER IMAGINE...XOXO

i believe in you

Contents

GRATITUDE

To my decade long best friend, my left hand man, the guy who juggled work, our one year old and two year old, remained committed to his eight week fitness goal, and still found time to come to visit me in hospital, Joshua. Thank you for your unconditional love, everything you do and have done for us. You have cracked me open, challenged me and pushed me to my absolute edge, every single day. Thank you for all of the life lessons we have learned together and our two glorious sons. I appreciate you. I love you.

My Darling Mother. You are my rock, my backbone, my soundboard, my biggest believer, and my "anything I need whenever I need it". Without a question of a doubt, your love, support and unwavering positivity has helped me through the toughest times of my life. You dropped everything to help our little family and take charge of my role from cooking to cleaning to washing to chasing after the babes and keeping me from spending too long at rock bottom. You saved me, you grew me, you birthed me and for all of this and so much more I will be eternally grateful to you.

To my big sister Sacha, for being the most exemplary role model a little sister could dream to look up to, thank you from the bottom of my heart for your unconditional love and for believing in me. And my big brother Aaron, thank you for finding me in any country around the world, getting me out of financial pickles and forever being the practical yin to my emotional yang. I love you guys.

To my Step Father Wayne. Thank you for allowing Mum to be so there for me as much as you do, supporting her, us and most of all, for loving our boys the way that you do. Oceans of gratitude.

My Soul Tribe. My Mutha Sistaz. My Girl Gang. My Guy Gang. Your unconditional love, words of inspiration, food in hospital, flower deliveries, floor mopping, shower assistance, home-made food for the entire family, unwavering support, the whole works. Your energy and belief in who I am and how strong I am is a reflection of you all. You are the wind beneath my wings, and I couldn't have made it this far in this glorious life without you and your belief in me. You all know who you are... each and every one of you sassy superhumans around the world.

Huge appreciation to all the staff that helped brighten my journey at Tweed Hospital. Thank you so much for saving my life, taking me for a wheelchair walk, giving me the "warm" blankets, leaving me hand-written notes of inspiration, play-ing old school rock and roll tunes to get me through. You are such incredible humans doing what you do. Utmost grati-tude to you all.

Deep reverence to my team behind the scenes; Isabelle—coach, web design, book cover design—thank you for creating a container within the container, for allowing me to show up as my fully expressed self, keeping me in check, & helping me figure out how to pull this all together. Simply put, I could not have done this without you. You are a super star. Kya—Artist, Dancer, Designer, Dreamer, Advocate for Healing, Mental Health & Nature. Thank you for your incredible works of art through this epic co-creation. You are magic in motion.

Stepha—You Devine Diva, Magik Making Photographer, Soul Ecoist, Creative Badass, Empowerment Kween, Pink Loving Dreamer. Eternal gratitude to you Soul Sister for capturing my pure essence as a human being.

Lastly, to my "SHEROES" (definition for those who don't know what SHEROES are—SHE HEROES). The beacons of light in my times of darkness who gave me an example of strong women to look up to and aspire to join, in the movement to empower others to live life on purpose. Thank you for your words of wisdom and inspiration before, after and during my dark days:

Joanne Rowling—Courageously Rocking Rock Bottom like a creative genius BOSS. **Inspiration.**

Gabrielle Bernstein—My Guru & Motivational ROCKSTAR who liberates on a global scale. **Spirituality.**

Brene Brown—Vulnerability, Boundaries, Rising Strong – Thank you for teaching me. **Boundaries.**

Jada Pinikett Smith—Motherhood, Marriage & Spirituality. Filling my cup first. Amen. **Sacrifice.**

Teresa Palmer—Total Bombshell, Mamma Bear & Biz Woman, Always putting family first. **Parenting.**

Constance Hall—Not taking myself too seriously in the Mayhem of Motherhood. **Laughter.**

Kris Carr—Ambitious, Down To Earth, Driven Goddess, Cancer Thriver, Healing Through Nutrition. **Healing.**

Beyoncé Knowles—Bringing killer dreams to life in impeccable style with utmost integrity. **Creation.**

FOREWORD

As a trainer it is always a pleasure when someone attends the courses I teach who has a beautiful energy, a real zest for life and is not afraid to speak their truth—that was Courtney. We quickly became friends and our relationship has blossomed into a beautiful friendship over the years.

More recently at our catch up on the Gold Coast, Courtney told me she had finished her book and asked if I would like to read it and share my thoughts. Knowing Courtney well at this stage, I was quite excited to read it. However, when she said it was called 'Rocking Rock Bottom', I wondered, 'When did you ever hit Rock Bottom?' When you see Courtney in her online video demonstrations you will know exactly what I mean.

Whilst Courtney was on the EFT and Matrix Re-Imprinting courses, she was able to heal some of her own past traumas, as she mentions in the book. However, I was not aware of the extent to which her health had declined and the many aspects of her experience that she had to endure and get through it all. This was undoubtedly a massive turning point in her life.

Reading her book has given me great insights into Courtney's life challenges- the good and the not so good, that has made her who she is today. I feel the book highlights how someone can come from their 'Rock Bottom' to leading a life of empowerment and living to the absolute fullest by having the scientifically proven tools and strategies she has used in her darkest moments.

I really like how Courtney has written her story as if she is speaking directly to you. Her story is woven between empowering quotes and easy, effective activations that everyone, myself included, can add to their toolbox of self-empowerment strategies.

Courtney is a true testament to how you can transform your life by using these techniques and tools. Who knows what she will achieve in the future, but I bet it will be extraordinary.

Caroline Dawson
EFT and Matrix Reimprinting International Trainer
Trainer of Trainers South East Asia
Founder of Matrix Past Life Reimprinting
Published Author

INTRO

The truth is, everyone's idea of rock bottom is different. Just like we are. For some it's reaching homelessness, for others it's the dismantling of a family, addiction, infidelity, health, prostitution, unemployment, bankruptcy. There should be no comparison as it is completely irrelevant. What is profoundly relevant is *what* we decide to do from here. Our very own "Rock Bottom."

This here story is a story of triumph. And not the kind of triumph that initially springs to your mind, like Harry Potter, saving the world from the evil that is Lord Voldemort. Cheers Harry, you are an all time hero on our big screen. Albeit an unreal story, this one here is a very REAL story. This is a story of a hero of a different kind. A hero of heart. A silent soldier. A weekend warrior. A triumph over trauma kind of victory. Your girl next-door, rising and falling through the seasons of life like everyone else. Until one day, ultimately facing her life changing catalyst, and rising like a phoenix from the ashes to step into the true purpose of her life. This is a story of a girl with sheer determination and commitment to a bigger, brighter, more fulfilling future, day-by-day, with many little right actions. That girl is me, Courtney Starchild. And this here is my story.

My catalyst experience, like many others, came from out of nowhere. One day I was at home with my fiancé Josh and our two little boys whilst experiencing a niggling sore throat. The next night

I was in hospital. Twelve days in total, five heavily sedated in the Intensive Care Unit, seven on the ward, two throat surgeries and ten whole days without seeing my beautiful baby boys. When I regained consciousness, the first thing I thought was, "Why aren't Josh and Mum one inch from my face?" I had no idea what had happened, no idea what day of the week it was, and certainly no idea what I was about to experience.

That night was the most harrowing and grueling night of my life and I will never forget how soul shattering the experience was. I literally had tubes coming in and out of every orifice. The pain and depletion setting in from 8 days being heavily dosed up and not moving was immeasurable. The sounds from the other darling hearts there in the ICU was gut wrenching. The energy alone was dark and dense. All the while, the most incredible humans on the planet, choosing to be there for work, helping humankind back from the brink. Bless their souls. I will forever be indebted to them, their selfless service and their loving, caring, compassionate nature.

It was alone, in the darkest of my dark days in that hospital that I decided enough was enough. I could not continue on as I had been in the past, focused on what I hadn't already achieved, constricted by my limiting beliefs of my worthiness of a better, more fulfilling life, pursuing what I truly loved, and nowhere near enough appreciation for all of the blessings currently present in my life. It was now time to completely recalibrate my mind, adjust my perspective and forge fiercely into the life I had always dreamed of. Just one day at a time. One small, right decision at a time.

"Now....

Slow down,

Get back on top of your health,

And go from there girl."

So on I went ... to ROCK MY ROCK BOTTOM.

CHAPTER 1

Going Gang Busters On Gratitude

LET'S HEAD BACK TO THE BEGINNING...

From as early as I can remember I felt very loved. I had a big sister and a big brother who doted on me. Seeing as they were nine and ten years older, I guess they saw me as their personal mascot and always made sure they fought over whose bed I would sneak into after a bad dream in the middle of the night. I look back on my childhood with them filled with loads of love, laughter and guidance. However, our childhood was not one that many would have wished for. We lived in a home fuelled by drama, deceit, infidelity, and consistent domestic violence. It was very common for us to be running away, temporarily staying at an Auntie's house or having police cars out the front of our house on the regular. Sometimes called by us, sometimes called by the neighbours due to the disturbance. Whilst this was a very unstable upbringing, it was all that we knew, and so it set the emotional tone for our childhood.

When I was twelve my parents finally broke up and it was a huge relief to me as there was no more fighting in our home. My sister and brother had moved out years before so it was just Mum and I now, and for the next three years we lived a very happy life together. Well, it was happy for me. I was enjoying all facets of life and school, achieving A's and B's on my report cards, Champion Girl of the Sports Carnivals, loving my friends, loving my social life and loving having my Mum all to myself. But it was a very challenging time for my mother on the other hand, who was lonely, not working, and sitting idle. We went on a trip to Bali when I was fifteen to buy a whole bunch of apparel for her friend to start a small business back in Perth, and shortly after, Mum moved to Bali in search of a better life. This completely changed the trajectory of my life. I say this for many reasons, one of which was because my year ten teacher had told me that I had received so many votes beyond the other nominees to be the year eleven school representative that he thought I was sure to be the head girl in year twelve. I then moved in with my father, his fiancé at the time and her three children who lived several suburbs away, so I had to change schools. I went from being on top of the world in all areas of my life to incredibly sad, isolated and unmotivated in a new environment full of people I didn't know and who didn't know me. The real me. The me before life got so off track. It was only a few short months later that my father's relationship came to a prompt end and he relocated to Queensland alone. Lucky for me this incredible woman, his now ex-fiancé, decided to take me under her wing and let me live in her family home with her and her three children for the next two years while I finished school. I thank the heavens every single day from the bottom of my heart for the blessing of my adopted family. It wasn't long after finishing school that my brother convinced me to move to Sydney to live with him. All I knew at that age was that when I finished school I wanted to travel and experience the world, so moving to Sydney felt like a step in the right direction.

I spent the next two years working my butt off with two jobs most of the time until I moved to Europe with my best friend Marnie at nineteen years old. We ran with the bulls, jumped off cliff faces, abseiled down Butterfly Valley, toured Anzac Cove, saw the most beautiful sights, made the most epic life-long friendships along the way and above all else, I fell head over heels in love with the most handsome man I had ever laid eyes on. Rafael. I had just finished work and headed out to a local club with a bunch of friends this particular evening. They were all mingling around the bar as I just stood leaning against a wall solo, a little tired and taking in the crowd. Then I saw him. Tall, dark and handsome. Long wavy brown hair tied back with a beautiful square jaw and brown eyes. I had to look away. What I didn't know at the time was that he had actually seen me a few weeks prior. I had been working in promotions on the streets of Lagos, Portugal when he saw me talking to his friend. Once his friend and I had finished speaking, Rafael asked his friend where I was from. When he discovered I was Australian and spoke English, he made it his mission to learn it. He went home that very night and told his identical twin brother Thiago (who DID speak English) that he had seen the most beautiful girl in the world and had decided to learn English so he could speak to her (next time he saw me). They were Brazilian and their whole family had pitched in money to send Rafael to Europe at nineteen years old so he could work and send money home to help support the rest of the family. A few months after Rafael had arrived he found a job, settled in and sent money back home for Thiago to then come and join him working. Back to the night we met,

I was leaning against a wall solo and Rafael had seen me. He told Thiago I was the girl he was talking about. Next thing you know Thiago was walking right towards me, taking his brothers opportunity. Now I didn't know these two were related, let alone identical twins. I thought they were just friends, so when Thiago came walking towards me, I thought to myself, "Well at least if I get chatting to this guy he might take me over to his group of friends and introduce me to the handsome fellow I had my eye on." Thiago arrived in front of me, asked how I was, what my name was and created some idle chitchat. After a short while he asked if I would like to join him for a dance. As a young girl when I attended my first Blue Light Disco my Mum said to me, "If any young man ever has the courage to ask you to dance, the least you can do is say yes. You don't need to dance for long, but the least you can do is say yes." So when Thiago asked, I said yes. The second he walked off in front of me to lead me to the dance floor I felt someone grab my hand from behind. It was Rafael. He said, "You wanna go beach," so I took his hand and followed him out of the club. Needless to say Thiago was not very impressed when he turned around and I had disappeared. Let alone when he found out later that I had disappeared with his identical twin brother Rafael. The rest is history.

Even my big brother got involved in the overseas escapades and he had an uncanny gift for finding me in foreign countries with very little information and even less contact. This may not seem like a big deal now but back before Facebook and everyone having a phone permanently attached to them, this was a big deal. I had emailed him to let him know I had found a job in Lagos, Portugal, at a bar called Joe's Garage. He happened to be in Europe himself, so decided he would make his way to Lagos and show up to the bar, sneak up behind me, cover my eyes and say, "What's a guy got to do to get a beer around here?" I jumped out of my skin, turned around, saw my big brother and threw my arms

Rafael graced this planet shining his light from 1983 – 2009

around him! There is nothing quite like the feeling of seeing family on the other side of the world in your alternate reality. It was pure magic. We danced the night away and I told him the campground in which we were living. He completely forgot which one but took to the streets in the morning to find me. He showed up to a campsite by the beach where he saw a handsome young man standing out the front of the campsite. He walked over and said, "You look like the kind of guy my sister would like, do you happen to know her? Her name is Courtney?" The young man replied, "Yeah, she is dating my identical twin brother." You might say he knew his little sister's weaknesses.

We spent the next few days enjoying each other's company before he was back on the road. A few months later when the work dried up in Lagos, my girlfriend and I moved to Luxembourg. I had once again emailed my brother to tell him that we had found work with a friend and landed the only apartment we could afford. It just so happened to be in the red-light district overlooking a strip joint called Studio 54 on the opposing side of the street. After a few weeks it became apparent to us that we were living in a brothel. On a Monday night when we weren't working, we would often sit in our studio with the lights off, looking across the road into the window of the club, watching all of the "performers" do drugs off of one another's bodies and get dressed. It was incredibly entertaining, such an unbelievable, true story, and I loved to wow my brother with the tales of my travels. Then one afternoon he was on a train passing through Luxembourg and decided, on a whim, to jump off and try to find me. No mobile phone, just an idea of the red-light district and Studio 54. If you have been to Luxembourg you will know it is a tiny country that you can drive through in 90 minutes just between Belgium, Germany and France. He jumped off the train, turned right and in a few streets found the red-light district. He eventually came to find studio 54 and started buzzing all of the intercoms when he remembered I said I could see INTO Studio 54. He ran across the road to our apartment building looking at each of the buzzer names. It wasn't hard to find us, seeing as the other intercoms had names like "Star", "Anastasia" and then us, "Oz Chix". He pressed our buzzer. Now, it was quite common for us to have multiple people ringing our doorbell during the week, (surprise surprise) and we would have to explain numerous times that we were, in fact, NOT "working girls". Hence, it was nothing out of the ordinary for me when the doorbell rang; it was however by incredible chance that I wasn't working this day and happened to be home, so answered with my usual "Yes?". My brother replied, "What's a guy got to do to get a beer around here?" and once again I jumped out of my skin. Four feet backwards actually, from the intercom speaker on the wall! That dodgy old lift couldn't get up to my floor fast enough. The doors opened and I flung my arms around him. I was elated to have my big brother back in my neck of the woods again. What a trip. What timing.

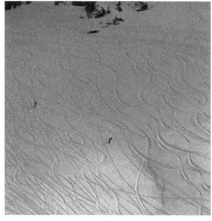

16

Travel & Love
ARE WORTH
The sacrifice
FOR A LIFE
Without Them
IS A LIFE UNEXPLORED

ATTICUS SAID THAT

After eighteen months of work and travel through Europe I returned to Sydney for a few years to "sort out my life", get my license and live in the real world. When I had checked those items off my list and saved some money, my closest friends and I headed off to Canada for a snow season and for me to learn how to snowboard. It was during these months in British Columbia that I had some of the best times of my life, shredding down those snow fields at the speed of light, tree runs and trekking off-piste, yet during that time I also realised that I was searching the world for something more. Belonging. Satisfaction. Fulfillment. Eventually I found myself enrolling in a Kundalini Yoga teacher training course in Kitsilano Vancouver. Looking back, I now know the course had been working its way towards me for some time prior to this. I can now see that the Day Spa that I was working at in Whistler held a special key to this path. And that key was in the form of a yoga DVD. There were a few DVDs to choose from and I specifically decided to go with the weirdest one, a Kundalini Yoga DVD by Gurmukh which had her wearing a white turban on the front cover, stating "As practised by Cindy Crawford and David Duchovney" – and to me that was one mega babe Super Model and one incredibly gifted actor from Californication who happened to remind me of my big brother. So that was it. Sold. A few months later, when I moved to Vancouver and started work, I began looking for a yoga teacher-training course close by. The only one that fit my work schedule and location was Kundalini Yoga at Yoga West, just a few short blocks from my apartment in Kitsilano. This was a life changing choice for me as I finally found something that satisfied my deep yearning for belonging and fulfilment. I finished my nine-month intensive teacher training, began intermittently rocking a turban while teaching and headed off to South America by myself for five months before eventually returning home to Australia.

20

Seven months after returning home I met Josh, the love of my life, and so began our crazy, challenging, passionate love affair. After five years on and off we decided to start a family and within fifteen months we had two young sons. Fast-forward a year of mothering two babes under the age of two, losing my identity along the way and taking my blessings for granted, I found myself lying helpless in a hospital bed after two unexpected throat surgeries. After ten days being heavily sedated I regained consciousness and was in extreme pain. I spent many hours during this time reflecting, thinking about my life, what had led me to this point and what it was that was truly important to me, and my happiness. It was in those dark hours of reflection that I rediscovered who I really was, what I stood for, and what I wanted to do with the rest of this human experience. My life.

"How did I get so lost?"

You see, typically I was your upbeat kind of girl who danced around the lounge room in her undies, sang full blast at the traffic lights, used sarcasm and humor to navigate life experiences and always tried to see the positive in any situation…. typically. But this wasn't my typical kind of experience and this drugged up, spaced out headspace was not my typical kind of headspace. There was some very unfamiliar territory to be covered, some extremely dark moments for me to work through and they all required me to choose mind over matter. That alone took every ounce of courage and strength that I had to conjure up.

Whilst I had spent nearly a decade practising and teaching Kundalini Yoga and Meditation, I still found myself struggling to reach a positive headspace during this time. Thoughts of

"This is so unfair"

"Why me?"

"Why does this keep happening to me?"

"Yet another setback"

"Just when I was about to teach again for the first time in years since having my babes"

"What the f*** is going on here?"

Your typical victim mentality. Certainly, no attitude of gratitude! Are you kidding me? The doctor said it was plain bad luck. Nothing I could have done to avoid this. He said, "Ten percent of people get tonsillitis, ten percent of that ten percent get Quinsy (which is a complication of tonsillitis and produces serious, even life-threatening complications including fluid accumulation around the heart, lungs, chest and difficulty breathing, which I had) and one percent, of that ten percent, of that ten percent get an abscess that requires two surgeries, one internal to take out the tonsils and one external to remove the abscess! HA! Lucky, I guess... Grateful, I guess?

I suppose I could be grateful for all the laughs the pain medication brought along with it though. One of the first doctors I had was just so kind, and sweet hearted, gentle and compassionate. However, I only saw him once and never caught his name. Such a bummer. The doctor I ended up having the entire time was very blunt and direct to say the least. I really had it in for him. As I couldn't talk due to the swelling in my throat and chest, I was scribbling pen on paper like a crazy woman. I was writing to Josh and Mum how I couldn't stand this doctor who was repeatedly making me cough and swallow (which I couldn't as I was in excruciating pain). I likened it to someone asking a patient with a broken leg to jump or run. After many days with the blunt doctor, I'd had enough and wanted to find this "Mc Dreamy" doctor whom I couldn't previously identify as I didn't know his name. I had been on so many medications I thought maybe I could draw a portrait, however this is not a talent I possess and needless to say the portrait did NOT help to identify the friendly doctor, as it was simply two abstract eyes and a line for a smile on an otherwise blank piece of paper. That got some pretty big belly laughs from the nurses and myself once I had made it through the other side of ICU. I suppose I am grateful for that.

When I initially woke up, I was struggling to get into a good headspace. It was black, I felt weak, I felt defeated, I was energetically contracting and I felt that blackness was washing over all the cells of my body. Not a great feeling at all. I was worried that "what you think you become" and I just wanted to bounce back and get the heck out of this ultraviolet lit, off time beeping, crazy environment as quickly as humanly possible. All I could do was try to visualise all the cells in my body, flourishing and blooming into the most colourful and luscious rainforest you ever did see. Kind of like in the movie Moana when Tefiti's heart is restored and she comes back to life reviving all the vegetation on the land. For anyone who doesn't have kids and hasn't seen that epic kids flick, you totally should. Anyway, I knew I wanted to become the strongest, most vibrant version of myself, so this was my starting point. Visualisation of cell replenishment and a perspective shift with a daily practice of the attitude of gratitude.

Now whilst the "attitude of gratitude" might sound cliché to some critics, it is backed by some of the most influential people of our time. Oprah Winfrey, Eckhart Tolle, Louise Hay, Deepak Chopra, Gabrielle Bernstein, Anthony Robbins, the list goes on. Not only do these tremendous role models support it, it is also backed by science. The revolutionary work of Dr Masuru Emoto, "The Hidden Messages in Water" outlines, "Molecules of water are affected by our thoughts, words and feelings." This is such potent information seeing as our planet and our human bodies are mostly comprised of water. "His book has the potential to profoundly change your worldview.

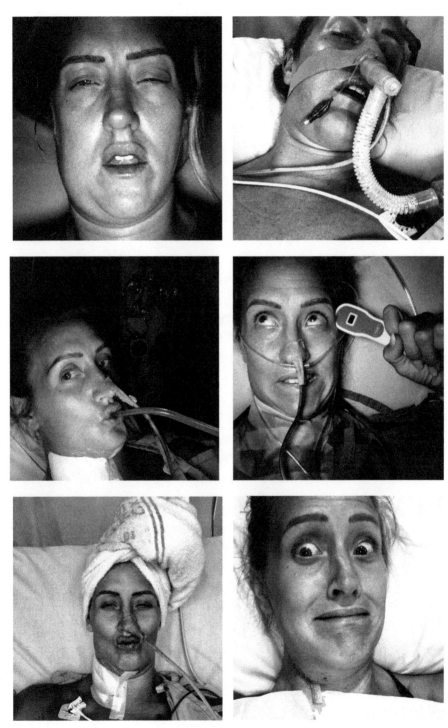

Snapshots of my hospital journey February 2018

Using high-speed photography Dr Masuru discovered that crystals formed in frozen water reveal changes when specific concentrated thoughts are directed towards them. He found that water from clear springs and water that had been exposed to loving words show brilliant, complex, colourful snowflake patterns. In contrast, polluted water or water exposed to negative thoughts forms incomplete, asymmetrical patterns with dull colors. The implications of this research create a new awareness of how we can positively impact the earth and our personal health." A few conclusions he made after decades of experimentation with water were:;

- Ailments are largely a result of negative emotions
- Immunity is both Love and Gratitude, and
- The Gratitude vibration/intention is more powerful and has greater influence over water

Below are two photographs taken after children at a Japanese elementary school spoke to the water. Take a close look at the difference in the formation of the crystals when positive words were spoken over the water versus the formation of the crystals when negative words were spoken over the water.

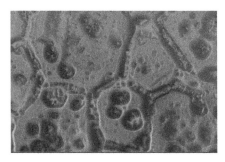

When the children said "You Fool" crystals did not form. Image; (C) Office Masaru Emoto, LLC

When the children said "You're Cute" perfect crystals formed. Image; (C) Office Masaru Emoto, LLC

Now take a moment to think about what you say to yourself when you look in the mirror.

Really think of the words, your thoughts, when you look yourself in the eyes, when you look at your body. What do you say? What do you think?

Let that sink in.

Think about the impact of these thoughts, feeling and words. Are these fresh, clean and clear thoughts creating positive flow through your human body? Would you say these things to your closest friends? To your parents? To your children? To your future children? If not, have some compassion for yourself and really have a think about what you just learned, make a decision to work on it from this moment forward and make that one small change. See what happens.

Acknowledging our current situation and headspace, accepting this, surrendering to this and readjusting this, is the first small but extremely significant and fundamental step you can take towards up-leveling your life. Appreciating yourself first, the lessons or blessings you have experienced in this life to form the person you are, and appreciating this miraculous world in which we get to live in and experience.

Albert Einstein, one of the most intelligent men of all time, once said, "There are only two ways to live your life. One is as though nothing is a miracle. The other is as though everything is a miracle." The latter is clearly apparent amongst astronauts who have experienced what they call "The Overview Effect" outlined in the documentary "Overview" on Vimeo. This is described as "a cognitive shift in awareness reported by astronauts during spaceflight, often while viewing the earth from orbit or from the lunar surface ...This state of mental clarity occurs when you are so far away from Earth that you become totally overwhelmed and awed by the fragility and UNITY of life on our blue globe." Ron Garan, a NASA Astronaut, experienced this when he traveled to the International Space Station. He said, "It really does look like this beautiful oasis in the middle of nothingness, and if you have a chance for your eyes to adjust you can actually see the stars and the Milky Way and it is an oasis on the backdrop of infinity. It really is a very moving experience to get to see that with your own eyes." To be able to have that kind of visceral experience, of such hindsight, such overview, you can come to understand that there is so much here for all of us to be grateful for, if we can simply gain the right perspective to see the forest for the trees.

An extremely life changing and self-empowering habit to help enable, and then build this "attitude of gratitude" and perspective (without going to the moon just yet) is committing yourself to a daily gratitude practice.

My two personal SHEROES I have to be grateful for...

Mum and I celebrating life post operation recovery. Thank you for everything you have done for me Mamma xx

My big sis and I reunited for the first time since my operations 6 months earlier.

Holistic Human Activation #1

Daily Gratitude Practice

This highly important tool I recommend is a journal for writing things we are grateful for down. Why? For reflection, growth, accountability, a sense of purpose and achievement. If I told you right now that this practice would take you only ten minutes a day to complete, yet make your overall life more enjoyable by 10%, would you do it? As we now know, there are vibrations in our words and power in those vibrations. We amplify their power when we write them down so why not try to create a new habit of waking up TOMORROW, writing down what you are grateful for and setting some intentions for the day, BEFORE picking up your phone? Start your day in PRO-ACTIVE mode, not RE-ACTIVE mode,

CREATIVITY BEFORE CONSUMPTION

See what happens. It is no coincidence that you are here reading this book. You know you want a better, more fulfilling life. This is your first step to showing up for yourself and creating that life! If you commit to this for 40 days I can guarantee you will be able to look back on when you started, how you felt, what you wrote down and be blown away by how much better you now feel having done this.

You have nothing to lose and absolutely everything to gain by Going Gangbusters On Gratitude!

If keeping a journal just isn't your thing and you genuinely feel you can't keep up with this practice, then implement an action plan that works for you. One gentleman used to keep a rock in his pocket each day and every time he would reach into his pocket for money or keys he would feel his rock and remember to tune in to the energy of gratitude by simply thinking of three things there and then that he was grateful for. You could do this, or something as simple as making it a daily ritual when you brush your teeth before bed to think of all the things that you are grateful for that day. Simple, profound and POWERFULLY LIFE CHANGING!

There are only

TWO WAYS TO

LIVE YOUR LIFE

ONE IS AS THOUGH NOTHING

IS A MIRACLE

THE OTHER IS AS THOUGH

Everything is a miracle

ALBERT EINSTEIN SAID THAT

Rehash

⭐ Acknowledge and appreciate your current situation

⭐ Visualize your healing and snapshot the feeling

⭐ Build your immunity through focus on what you love and have gratitude for

⭐ Open your mind to perceive all miracles and enhance your attitude of gratitude

⭐ Use these tools to build your new positive habits by implementing a daily gratitude practice

⭐ Share your story, journey, experiences, breakdowns and breakthroughs with each other on The Rocking Rock Bottom FB Page

CHAPTER 2

The Potent Power of Now

BOY DO I HAVE A STORY FOR YOU FOLKS

It was around June 2018 that I felt called to write this book about my experience in hospital and try to help others to see the silver lining of their challenging circumstances. Maybe even leverage the same tools of empowerment that helped me too. I started working on the content and structure, then had to put things on the back burner as our wedding was fast approaching in August. Once life had settled back down post wedding, I organised a weekend away from the hubby and the children to really try to make some headway with my writing. Unfortunately, our dog Ralphie suddenly became ill and we had no other choice but to put him down that evening. We had him for nine years, so I decided it was best to reschedule my weekend away and spend the rest of the weekend with our little family. Had this been prior to my hospital experience this would have made me extremely frustrated with its timing to experience "yet another setback"; instead I chose to view this as an opportunity to detour in the right direction and go with the flow of things. A few weeks later I managed to reorganise the time and headed down to a glorious little Gypsy Caravan in Bangalow, New South Wales.

Janette's Gypsy Caravan down in Bangalow New South Wales Australia.

I didn't bother to set an alarm that night as I am usually up with my babes at 5am, so I hit the sack early and had the best night's sleep. Eleven hours in fact. I woke up, tucked into some yoga and meditation, had a delicious home cooked breakfast, then jumped right in. One of the things I love so much about meditation—aside from all of its epic side effects of course—is that anybody can do it, it is non-denominational, it is FREE and you can access that infinite, ever loving source any time of the day or night, 365 days a year, 7 days a week. It is simply stilling your mind to connect with spirit. Whatever that means for you. Anyway, by 6pm I was happy with my first chapter and signed off for the evening. The next morning, I woke up bright and early and got stuck back in. By 1pm I took off for lunch as I needed a break and was close to completing chapter two. When I returned, I saw that my laptop (which had recently been on the fritz) had turned itself off. I turned it back on only to find that my whole day's work had been completely deleted. I couldn't believe it. I sat there for a moment reflecting on the irony of the situation and had to laugh. There I was, in Bangalow, pouring my heart and soul out onto some paper about how important "The Potent Power Of Now" is and NOW I was having a divine intervention to really take a sip of my own medicine. Classic Murphy's Law. Don't get me wrong, I was still slightly jilted about the whole experience, but there was nothing I could do about what had already happened. So, I decided to accept what was, pack up early, wind down my windows and drive the scenic route home with the wind in my hair to enjoy the rest of the afternoon with all three of my babes. What a trip. What a choice. What a lesson. Salute.

Now it's one thing to embrace something such as the above situation in our stride, it is however a completely different story embracing the potent power of now when you are feeling physically, mentally and emotionally weak and broken. It was only a few hours after I had woken up in the ICU that Mum and Josh had to leave and Nora, my soul saving nurse, asked if I would like to have a shower. "Yes please," I replied, and she left on a mission and returned shortly after with a walking frame and a lovely orderly named Les. Nora asked if I would like to try to walk to the bathroom using the walking frame. "Why not?" I said, so up Les helped me, and nothing. I couldn't move. I held onto the frame, but I couldn't lift my legs at all. They were so frail, and I was extremely weak. I sat back down on the bed and burst into tears. I felt so completely defeated. I mean, they wouldn't have offered me a walking frame if they didn't think I would actually be able to walk, would they? Surely not? Why couldn't I walk? After all, I had driven myself to the hospital. I could walk when I arrived there? I was devastated. Nora wheeled me off to the shower, and there I sat, naked in the wheelchair, unable to move, tubes in and out of every orifice, sobbing as she hosed me down. I had never felt this close to death in my life. Nora stood there patiently for the best part of an hour. The fear of not being able to swallow kept me awake most of that night. I think I may have dozed off for no more than two hours in total that entire time. I had too much to live for to die here. The thoughts of Josh and our children kept me clinging on to the hope that this surely was not the end.

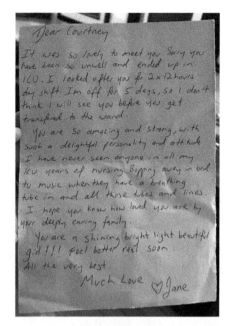

Jane, Tweed Heads ICU Nurse letter to Courtney.

The next day when Josh returned, it felt like an eternity since I had last seen him. Every minute seemed like an hour in there. I just wanted to hold him. We discussed the magnitude of our experience and he shared what he had been going through with the kids since I had arrived and undergone the two surgeries. We cried together and acknowledged just how lucky we were to have one another and to love one another as we do. I told him that our family was the most important thing in the world to me and that I now wanted to have another two children. You should have seen the look on his face. Lucky for him that was the drugs talking! I was still feeling pretty down in the dumps about the fact that I couldn't stand up and walk to the bathroom when Josh asked if I remembered Jane. She was one of the sweetheart nurses who had looked after me on the ward the days leading up to my first operation. I felt bad at this point because I couldn't remember her.

38

Josh reached into my bag and pulled out a letter she had written to me. It read;

Dear Courtney,

It was so lovely to meet you.

Sorry you have been so unwell and ended up in ICU.

I looked after you for 2 x 12 hours day shift.

I'm off for five days so I don't think I will see you before you get transferred to the ward.

You are so amazing and strong with a delightful personality and attitude.

I have never seen anyone in all my ICU years of nursing bopping away in bed to music when they have a breathing tube in and all those tubes and lines.

I hope you know how loved you are by your deeply caring family.

You are a shining bright light beautiful girl!!!

Feel better real soon.

All the very best.

Much Love

Jane

I remembered rocking away in bed to some sweet tunes (like Ambala "Walk With The Dreamers" and Angie McMahon "Slow Mover" on repeat) and was so moved that a nurse had taken the time to write such a lovely note for me that I burst into tears again. What an absolute sweetheart. I couldn't believe that I had slipped back into this "woe is me" headspace once more. That wasn't me. I was determined to shake that off. Mind you, the nurses DID tell me that while I was on the ward for observation, pre-operations, that I had enough sedatives for four people and they still couldn't knock me out. I remembered scribbling on my paper that I was "Rocky Balboa and my theme song was 'The Eye of The Tiger' and no one could knock me out!" What a total goose. Considering this, and with all of the drugs from the time I entered the hospital on Friday evening until I woke up the following Saturday, it was no wonder my head was all over the place.

42

Only in my pain
DID I FIND MY WILL

Only in my chaos
DID I LEARN TO BE STILL

Only in my fear

DID I LEARN MY MIGHT

Only in my darkness

DID I SEE MY LIGHT

T.M.T SAID THAT

At this point we were still uncertain how much longer I was going to be in hospital. It depended on my recovery and strength, so I wanted to try to focus on what I could do to get the wheels in motion for this speedy recovery. That day we were going to introduce soft foods and fluids. I was so pumped. I messaged Mum who made a chicken vegetable soup to bring in. Bless her cotton socks. When she arrived, she gave me the soup and told me of a "Tapping Summit" about energy healing that I should watch with my time in ICU. I had a quick look and thought the whole thing looked a bit weird to me and left it at that. In the meantime, one of the nurses brought me a tray with a handful of different soft foods and fluids to try. OH MY LORD! A cup of tea!! That was definitely going to warm the cockles of my heart! I poured the hot water, steeped my tea, added my milk and voila! Time to enjoy. Except I didn't enjoy it at all, it was completely horrendous. So horrendous I almost spat it out. My taste buds were seriously out of whack. I tried a sip of apple juice and it too tasted terrible. Everything tasted like mucous. AHHHHH!! What was happening? I was so excited to eat and drink and nothing tasted good. Not even Mum's delicious homemade soup. And again I slipped back into my pity party.

Those early days in recovery were an insane roller coaster ride of emotions. Whilst I was consciously trying to be grateful for the lessons I was learning, the drugs were amplifying all of my emotions. I simply had to try my best to surrender to the experience and continuously remind myself that, "This too shall pass". What I didn't realise at the time was that this journey was exactly what I needed to experience to catapult me out of the complacency I had morphed into in my everyday life. I will say it again, it is extremely difficult to acknowledge this when you are neck deep in the thick of things. It takes a lot of acceptance and patience to honour your current challenging experiences and view them as growth mechanisms for the person you are here to become. Louise Hay says, "The point of power is in the present moment. Right here and right now in our own minds. It does not matter how long we have had negative patterns, or an illness, or a rotten relationship, or lack of finances, or self-hatred, we can begin to make a change today. The thoughts we have held and the words we have repeatedly used have created our life and experiences up to this point. Yet, that is past thinking, we have already done that. What we are choosing to think and say, today, this moment, will create tomorrow and the next day, and the next week and the next month and the next year, etc."

It is a conscious choice. A repeated choice. Every day. Every challenge. Every moment. A choice of love over fear. Every single time. Each time you choose love you win. You are working in unison with the universe. The more you align with the abundant and infinite energy of the universe, the more synchronicity you experience, and so ensues the serendipity of synchronicity! A.K.A. Awesome things happening one after the other in a really cool and beneficial way.

BOOM! Yes please. And did someone just say all I have to do is choose love? I can do that.

We have all experienced that feeling when you wake up before your alarm, put your jeans on to find some cash in your pocket, you jump in your car and get every green light, park your car and the meter is already paid. HECK YASSSS! This is how things started to unfold for me when I finally got out of hospital. I had been committing to my daily meditation practice. I was giving gratitude as often as possible, for everything, my health, my family, my friends. Anything and everything I could see, feel and experience. I was a magnet for magnificence. I started diving deep into books and courses that the universe was sending my way. I told Josh while I was still in hospital that I wanted us to set some strategic goals for our future (goal setting was pretty standard for me, however, I wanted more strategy, structure and guidance.) I searched online and found an epic, well-defined goal setting course over in the states for a huge sum of money. There was absolutely no way I could get to the states let alone afford to do that. Some months earlier I had subscribed to an online newsletter. I had seen Michael Beckwith, a Visionary from the movie "The Secret" featured on one of the business show reels which piqued my interest, so I subscribed. Up until this point I hadn't engaged with any content until I came out of hospital. My inbox had a newsletter; I opened it and it happened to be a course in strategic goal setting for a tiny fraction of the price of the one I had seen in that states! I couldn't believe it! What were the chances? I was so blown away and excited that I signed up right there and then. Over the coming weeks I really immersed myself in this course. I went to Sydney for my birthday and got together with a bunch of girlfriends. One of my friends had just finished her Degree in Naturopathy and I was telling her all about this incredible goal setting framework I was currently exploring. She was telling me all about her course and a fantastic hypnotherapist she had been learning about. I returned home a few days later and that week another email popped up in my inbox with a free master class by the hypnotherapist she was telling me about. I mean come on... Seriously? Now I was even more blown away and of course I did the master class, it was FREE! The whole thing was by complete fluke as it was on a day that I had both my babes at home by myself and by pure chance that they both went down to sleep at the same time. This was really what allowed me to take the class. Usually when you try to orchestrate plans such as this based on children's nap times you can most certainly guarantee that something disturbs the system and therefore disturbs your otherwise rock-solid plan. Have kids they said, it would be fun they said, Ha Ha Ha. I love those little guys.

IT DOESNT

Take Time

IT TAKES

Alignment

ABRAHAM HICKS SAID THAT

49

Now a little back-story to show you that when the time is right and you are truly aligned things will come in to flow and work in your favour. About six months prior to all of this I had been reading one of my "Sheroes" books, Gabby Bernstein's "The Universe Has Your Back." It was quite interactive and had me acknowledge my belief system, define it, curate what it was I wanted to attract into my life and how to best perceive the obstacles along the way. As I was currently still working through my goal setting framework it became evident that one goal I wanted to achieve was to write a book about overcoming my catalyst experience. I decided to share this new goal with Josh, my fiancé, who completely blew me away when he said he thought it was the best idea I had ever told him. Anyone who knows me, knows I have a lot of ideas, so I was feeling particularly encouraged by his support. That week I began writing out my S.M.A.R.T (specific, measurable, achievable, rewarding, time bound) goals regarding my book completion deadline, how many pages I wanted to write in total and how many I would have to write each week to achieve this goal. That week another email popped up in my inbox. This time it was from Gabby Bernstein. She was releasing her annual Master Class Course next month all about building your business and book writing. No. Freaking. Way. This was totally on point with everything I was consciously working towards creating in my life. I finished my goal-setting course just in the nick of time and started this next one. What I didn't know was that there was also a module included in this Master Class course on The Emotional Freedom Technique, also known as "Tapping". The very technique my mother had suggested to me months earlier in hospital. With everything that had been falling into place over the last few months and leading me on this path of healing, I was now in a far better place, with the right mindset and the right timing, to really open my mind to experimenting with this new healing tool before me.

Without a question of a doubt, I truly believe that my daily practices were the tools of empowerment that cleared the path for the above serendipity of synchronicity to this point. A very powerful tool that you can use to start to help you accept your current circumstances (whatever they may be) and empower your "present AND future self" to call on the life you truly deserve to live, is breath work. I want you to start with this very simple and easy tool, then later on in the book we can step you into some of the more involved practices. This practice is to gently teach you how to detach from your thoughts and get into a calm, still mental state to allow for deep parasympathetic nervous system healing. At first your mind will be very busy, I want you to think about how you would decide to spring clean and how your house will get far messier first, before you clear everything out and get to experience the nice clean state you are working towards. It is the same with your mind and thoughts. Your brain has been programmed your whole life to have thoughts and you respond to them emotionally. You are just beginning now to consciously acknowledge these, train your brain and make the necessary changes. Go easy on yourself. When you notice the mind going off track, simply return to the breath and repeat this training as you would weights training, getting stronger, bigger, bolder and longer in your practice. I like to set an alarm if I am on a time frame so I don't get distracted. That way I can allow myself to really get lost in the clearing energy of the breath. Ideally you want to build up your practice over time. You will be surprised how much you come to love and crave this practice.

Holistic Human Activation #2

Breath Work

Simple Alternate Nostril Breathing.

First up, take note of how you are currently feeling. Take a few deep breaths. Acknowledge where you are at.

Posture

In any comfortable position with the spine straight

Eyes

Closed and focused at the third eye point where the brows meet

Mudra

Right index finger and middle finger rested on third eye point

Breath

Cover your right nostril with your right thumb. Inhale a slow, long, deep breath through your left nostril, then block the left nostril with your right ring finger, release the right thumb, exhale a slow, long, deep breath through your right nostril. Inhale right nostril slow, long and deep. Block right nostril, release left nostril, exhale left. Think of a U shape, up one nostril, out the other, up that nostril then out the other.

Duration

Repeat for 5 minutes to begin with, nice long, slow, deep breaths. Once you have repeated your cycle for 5 minutes you can complete the exercise with ten long deep inhale/exhales through both nostrils then sit and vibrate in this space. Over time you can build this up to 11 minutes then to 21 minutes.

To End

Once completed, I want you to take a snapshot of how you are feeling and stay in that vibration for as long as possible. This is a great time to also think of all the blessings in your life that you are grateful for. As you go about the rest of your day, I invite you to try to recall this feeling as often as possible and see how long you can remain here. This is a fantastic way to build up your connection to this infinite source of energy and healing to be able to completely transform your physical and mental health, let alone your entire life in general. You can also find a demonstration of this at www.courtneystarchild.com/universe

Scientific Benefits

- Inhaling through the left nostril triggers the rest/relaxation response (parasympathetic nervous system) and inhaling through the right stimulates the fight/flight response (sympathetic nervous system). This means by choosing which nostril you use to inhale, you can make yourself either more relaxed (left nostril) or more energised (right nostril)

- Balancing the activity between your left and right nostril brings the sympathetic and parasympathetic nervous system into equilibrium
- Pulse rate and respiratory rate slow down significantly
- Reduces systolic and diastolic blood pressure immediately after
- Improves cardiovascular function
- Reduces stress and anxiety
- Improves lung function & respiratory endurance
- Promotes overall well being

Rehash

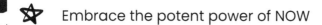

★ Embrace the potent power of NOW

★ Choose LOVE over FEAR... EVERYTIME

★ Remember you are being divinely guided

★ Practise your Breath Work

★ Snapshot the feeling—Tune into it throughout the day

★ Share your story, journey, experiences, breakdowns and breakthroughs with each other on the Rocking Rock Bottom FB Page

The Universe

IS ALWAYS SPEAKING TO US

Sending us little messages

CAUSING COINCIDENCES

And serendipities reminding us

TO STOP TO LOOK AROUND

To believe in something else

SOMETHING MORE

NANCY THAYER SAID THAT

CHAPTER 3

Conquering Your Badass Consciousness

THE ULTIMATE LIFE QUEST

Doesn't that sound like a thrilling adventure to take on? An Ultimate Life Quest. Except if you remove the sizzling headline and take it for what it really is, conquering your consciousness isn't a THRILLING adventure or something you can tick off your "to do" list. In actual fact it is a way of life. It's messy, it's tough AF and it's ugly. It takes a bucket load of commitment, surrender, vulnerability, trust, determination and consistent, continual, concentrated effort to build this everyday ritual so you can reap the deep, soul satisfying benefits of being bulletproof, unf*ckwithable, aligned, connected and fulfilled on the reg. I'm not here to sugar coat it for you baby. I am here to be REAL, to cheer you on, and to show you that with long term, consistent, right actions, you too can achieve your wildest dreams. NO BS. It starts with a few key principles:

- Cultivating Your Awareness
- Emotional Education
- Trigger Transformation

It is easy and extremely common to react, engage and retaliate when we become emotionally hooked which is why we need loads of practice of being conscious of our thoughts. It takes a very skilled, grounded, consciously aware human to be able to acknowledge when something has affected them emotionally, stop in their tracks, breathe, notice the physiological changes, increased heart rate, sweaty palms, frown, (whatever it is for each individual) disrupt that process, breathe again, and curiously ask themselves what they are feeling and why they are feeling it. At the end of the day we are all human beings and our emotional reactions are very "human." So this cultivation of awareness doesn't mean you won't ever react again; it is the lifelong practice of really getting to know yourself and better managing your thoughts, your feelings, your emotions and your reactions. So why exactly is this practice of such ASTRONOMICAL importance to you, your life, your health, your happiness and your future? I'm glad you asked precious soul...

Cultivating your awareness is all about catching yourself in the act of thinking and reacting so you can disrupt your fight or flight response and retrain your brain otherwise. What is emotion? It is energy in motion, so when someone or something sets off an emotional response in you, your brain fires off a bunch of neurons, which are nerve cells that carry information from the brain to the rest of the body. Our brains were built to overreact to a perceived threat. The same neuronal machinery that protected our ancestors from charging lions around two hundred thousand years ago is now locked

60

and loaded today with a brain double the size and an emotional capacity three times the size, yet now it's dealing with multiple ordinary stresses everyday like traffic, work, socials, etc. We haven't yet had a "Software Update" even though our brain has near tripled in size. So your body releases the hormone cortisol; this sets off the brain's alarm bells by stimulating the emotionally charged amygdala (the amygdala is an almond-shape set of neurons located deep in the brain, shown to play a key role in the processing of emotions) and all the while damaging neurons in the hippocampus. This shrinks the calming part of the brain that puts things into perspective and regulates our emotions. What that means is when you activate your amygdala with your emotions the rational part of your brain turns off as you launch into flight, fight or freeze mode. So many people in today's society spend years living in this constant state of stress unknowingly and eventually reach complete emotional and physical fatigue, sometimes even a total breakdown. Therefore, if something upsets you and you can acknowledge your feelings, experience them, sit with them and breathe through them, then you have just disrupted your natural neurological pathway of simple "reaction" and from here you can start to rewire your brain by just "being aware" of what happens for you in your body when you become emotionally engaged. This is key to becoming bulletproof.

Emotional education and articulation have got to be one of the most fundamental areas for development of our species. Most commonly when people are unable to communicate or articulate exactly how they are feeling about an experience or a situation they become even angrier and more frustrated, which then further aggravates the situation and the people involved. Brene Brown, another one of my SHEROS, explains her data results around emotional awareness, saying, "The average person can describe three emotions. Happy, sad

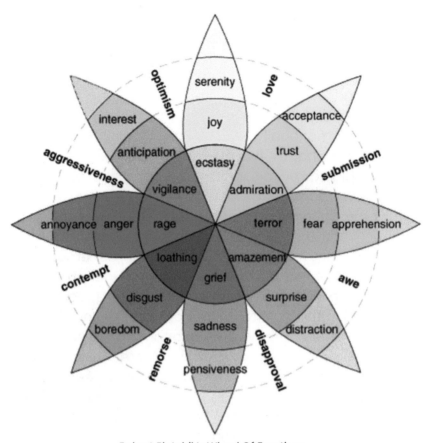

Robert Plutchik's Wheel Of Emotions

and pissed off, yet we have around thirty we need to be able to articulate." What a humongous gap.

Above is a wheel of emotions with 29 outlined emotions for you to familiarise yourself with and start trying to use to specifically articulate in a more granular way how you are feeling from now on.

Trigger transformation involves your initial practice of awareness, so you acknowledge your emotions have come up, you ask yourself what you are feeling, you identify these emotions as you are feeling them (because you are now learning more than just your average three commonly identified emotions), you sit with these feelings, experience their normalcy and then you ask yourself WHY? Why am I so annoyed with WHAT this person has said or done? This is when we really start to uncover our true triggers and our deep-set subconscious belief systems.

Subconscious programs run 95-99% of our daily behaviour. Many of these negative programs were imprinted in the first six years of your life based on trauma, misperceptions and observing those around you. Quantum Physicists talk of an energetic field surrounding us, the Quantum Field also known as The Matrix where these negative subconscious programs, based on images of past events, are held in our local fields and regarded subconsciously as current events. This is how we can continually deplete our nervous system by being catapulted into fight, flight or freeze mode repeatedly when we are emotionally triggered with similar events today and react based on old subconscious belief systems in the way we would have at the age we first experienced these events. It is quite confronting when we peel back the onion layers to really uncover what the truth is about our subconscious behavioural patterns and what we are experiencing and then reacting to. It doesn't mean we won't ever be triggered again, as I said earlier, it just means we can be more prepared in the future on how to better acknowledge these emotions in these situations when they arise, so we can get curious about what's happening to us emotionally, remind our primitive brain that "Hey, we are not under attack by charging lions", and we can simply pack away the cortisol, breathe this one out and behave like the evolved humans that we are becoming, today. YIEW! An incredibly talented young psychologist once told me, "When we are children, we create coping mechanisms for certain circumstances. As we grow through our teen years these coping mechanisms still work and we are mostly resilient. As we progress through our twenties, we are broadening our horizons, experimenting, living life and learning about ourselves. Usually by the time we reach our thirties, we are experiencing a whole new world in our relationships, becoming parents and evolving even further when we realise our old coping mechanisms are now completely worn out and it is time to upgrade and find new coping mechanisms, tools and processes that will work for us."

The relevance of these wholesome practices to you right now, your life, your health, your happiness and your future, come down to what Dr Joe Dispenza explains in his book "Becoming Supernatural". "Emotions are chemical feedback, the end products of experiences we have in our external environment. So, as we react to a situation in an external environment, that produces an emotion. The resulting internal chemistry can signal our genes to either turn on (up-regulating or producing an increased expression of the gene) or to turn off (down regulating or producing a decreased expression of the gene). The gene itself doesn't physically change—the expression of the gene changes, and that expression is what matters most because that is what affects our health and our lives. Thus, even though someone may have a genetic disposition for a particular disease, for example, if their genes continue to express health instead of expressing that disease, they won't develop the condition and will remain healthy."

So if we can acknowledge our challenging life circumstances, embrace them as lessons, feel our natural emotions, acknowledge that what we feel is completely normal and often warranted, then breathe through the feelings, learn about them, comfort ourselves, let the attachment to the negative emotions go and then call upon forgiveness, love and gratitude to heal ourselves and attract more of the same, we can soon become the masters of our own DNA destiny. I know it might sound farfetched to begin with but the more you learn, the more you realise that the scientific proof and

Yogi Bhajan – Master of Kundalini Yoga

the mind-blowing results of numerous patients around the world who have completely healed themselves from incurable diseases is no coincidence. They have tapped into the body's immeasurable, innate ability to heal itself by starting with the mind. The more we fill our lives with positive experiences and positive people who trigger positive emotions for us, the more we will heal ourselves, attract more health, more happiness and inevitably live life with more harmony.

Yogi Bhajan, a Master of Kundalini Yoga who brought it to the west said this following meditation was one of three, that if all other teachings were lost, this was one to see us through The Aquarian Age, the one we are in right now. This ultimate tool of empowerment is one of my favourite meditations because for an active mind like mine there is a lot to focus on, four components in fact; mantra (spoken word), mudra (hand signals), voice volume and visualisation. The rewards of this long-term practice are supremely profound, as you will experience throughout your own practice.

Music

AND MEDITATION

HAVE ALWAYS BEEN MY

Medicine

I SAID THAT – ITS KINDA MY JAM

Holistic Human Activation #3

Meditation

Monkey Mind Meditation

Posture

In easy pose, cross legged or sitting however possible with a nice long straight spine. That's your antenna for connecting to your higher self

Eyes

Closed and focused at the third eye point

Mantra

This kriya uses the five primal sounds, or the Panj Shabd—S, T, N, M, A

In the original *bij* form of the word Sat Nam

SAA: Infinity, cosmos, beginning

TAA: Life, existence

NAA: Death, change, transformation

MAA: Rebirth

This is the cycle of creation. From the Infinite comes life and individual existence. From life comes death or change. From death comes rebirth of consciousness. From rebirth comes the joy of the Infinite through which compassion leads back to life. *SAA TAA NAA MAA*

Mudra

Each repetition of the entire mantra takes 3 to 4 seconds

The elbows are straight while chanting. Hands in Gyan Mudra (pointy finger touching with the thumb). Then each finger touches, in turn, the tip of the thumb with a firm but gentle pressure.

SAA: The index or Jupiter finger touches the thumb

TAA: The middle or Saturn finger and thumb

NAA: The ring or Sun finger and thumb

MAA: The pinkie or Mercury finger and thumb

Then begin again with the index finger

Visualisation

You must meditate on the primal sounds in the "L" form. This means that when you meditate you feel there is a constant inflow of cosmic energy into your solar centre, or Tenth Gate (The Crown Chakra). Chakra Chart for your reference on page 80-81. As the energy enters the top of the head, you place Sa, Ta, Na, Ma there. As you chant Sa for example, The "S" starts at the top of your head and the "A" moves down and out through the Brow Point, projected into infinity. This energy flow follows the energy pathway called the golden cord—the connection between the pineal and pituitary gland. Some people may occasionally experience headaches from practising Kirtan Kriya if they do not use the "L" form. The most common reason for this is improper circulation of *prana* to the solar centres.

Voice

The mantra is chanted in the three languages of the consciousness;

- **Aloud** (the voice of the human) awareness of the things of the world
- **Whisper** (the voice of the lover)   experiencing the longing to belong
- **Silent** (the voice of the divine)   meditate on Infinity or mentally vibrate

Duration

Sit straight in Easy Pose and meditate at the Brow Point

Chant aloud for **5 minutes**

Then whisper for **5 minutes**

Then go deeply into silence, mentally vibrating the sound for **10 minutes**

Then whisper for **5 minutes**

Then chant aloud **5 minutes**

To End

Close the meditation with a deep inhale and suspend the breath as long as comfortable—up to a minute—relaxing it smoothly to complete one minute of absolute stillness and silence. Then stretch the hands up as far as possible spread the fingers wide. Stretch the spine and take several deep breaths. Relax. You can also find a demonstration of this over at the online edition www.courtneystarchild.com/universe.

Comments

Each time the mudra is closed by joining the thumb with a finger, the ego "seals" the effect of the mudra in the consciousness. The effects are as follows;

SIGN	FINGER	NAME	EFFECT
Jupiter	Index	Gyan Mudra	Knowledge
Saturn	Middle	Shuni Mudra	Wisdom, intelligence, patience
Sun	Ring	Surya Mudra	Vitality, energy of life
Mercury	Pinkie	Buddhi Mudra	Ability to communicate

Practising this meditation brings a total mental balance to the individual psyche. As you vibrate on each fingertip, you alternate your electrical polarities. The index and ring fingers are electrically negative, relative to the other fingers. This causes a balance in the electro-magnetic projection of the aura. If during the silent part of the meditation your mind wanders uncontrollably, go back to a whisper, to a loud voice, to a whisper and back to silence.

Do this as often as necessary to stay alert. Practising this meditation is both a science and an art. It is an art in the way it moulds consciousness and the refinement of sensation and insight it produces. It is a science in the tested certainty of the results it produces. Each meditation is based on the tested experience of many people, in many conditions, over many years. It is based on the structure of the psyche and the laws of attraction and reaction that accompany each sound, movement and posture. The meditations as *kriyas* code this science into specific formulas we can practise to get specific results. Because it is so effective and exact, it can also lead to problems if not done properly. Chanting the *Panj Shabd*—the primal or nuclear form of *Sat Nam*, into its primary elements.

You may use this chant in any position as long as you adhere to the following:

1. Keep the spine straight
2. Focus at the brow point where the centre of your brows meet
3. Use the "L" form of meditation
4. Vibrate the Panj Shabd in all three languages—human, lover and divine
5. Use common sense without fanaticism

The timing can be decreased or increased as long as you maintain the ratio of spoken, whispered and silent chanting—always end with one minute of complete stillness and silence.

Scientific Benefits

The Alzheimer's Research and Prevention Foundation found the following scientific benefits of the consistent practice of Kirtan Kriya:

- Improved memory
- Reduced stress
- Enhanced Brain Blood Flow
- Increased Healthy Brain Size
- Improved Brain Chemistry
- Increased Telomerase (parts of genes that keep you young)
- Decrease in bad genes
- Improvement of good genes
- Improved Sleep
- Less Depression
- Clarity of Purpose
- Spiritual Well Being

Rehash

★ Cultivate awareness

★ Educate yourself emotionally

★ Train your triggers towards curiosity

★ MEDITATE

★ Rinse and repeat as often as possible.

★ Share your story, journey, experiences, breakdowns and breakthroughs with each other on the Rocking Rock Bottom FB Page

The 7 Chakras For Beginners

Location on the body

7 — Crown Chakra

6 — Third Eye Chakra

5 — Throat Chakra

4 — Heart Chakra

3 — Solar Plexus Chakra

2 — Sacral Chakra

1 — Root Chakra

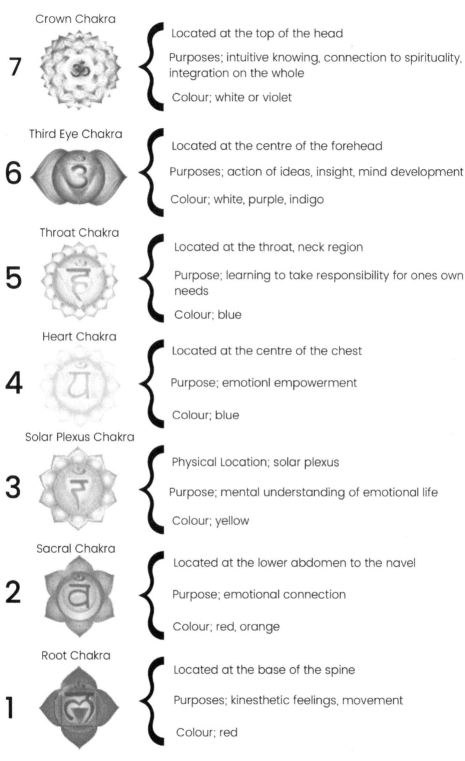

Crown Chakra

7

- Located at the top of the head
- Purposes; intuitive knowing, connection to spirituality, integration on the whole
- Colour; white or violet

Third Eye Chakra

6

- Located at the centre of the forehead
- Purposes; action of ideas, insight, mind development
- Colour; white, purple, indigo

Throat Chakra

5

- Located at the throat, neck region
- Purpose; learning to take responsibility for ones own needs
- Colour; blue

Heart Chakra

4

- Located at the centre of the chest
- Purpose; emotionl empowerment
- Colour; blue

Solar Plexus Chakra

3

- Physical Location; solar plexus
- Purpose; mental understanding of emotional life
- Colour; yellow

Sacral Chakra

2

- Located at the lower abdomen to the navel
- Purpose; emotional connection
- Colour; red, orange

Root Chakra

1

- Located at the base of the spine
- Purposes; kinesthetic feelings, movement
- Colour; red

The problem

IS NOT

The problem

THE PROBLEM IS

Your attitude

ABOUT THE PROBLEM

CAPTAIN JACK SPARROW SAID THAT

CHAPTER 4

Crystal Clear Certainty With Conviction

ALLOWING YOUR MESS TO BECOME YOUR MESSAGE

Do you know who you truly are and what you really want out of life? I surely didn't. I was one of those girls who envied the astronauts or doctors who would say "Ever since I was four I wanted to be a *(insert specific occupation here) when I grew up!" How awesome I thought? To know with such conviction from such a young age and spend your whole life working towards that incredible goal. There was so much I loved to do, learn and experience growing up that I had trouble deciding exactly what industry or education would best suit me, my personality and my ambitions. When I moved to Sydney I started working in retail and quickly found the industry to be a little too cutthroat for my liking. Maybe not the industry as a whole but the store in which I worked in certainly was; not only that, but I could be making almost double my paycheck for the same hours working in hospitality. So off I went and pounded the pavement with my resume. I was fierce with my follow up phone calls to the prospective employers and getting on a first name basis with all of their receptionists. "Even though I have no experience, I know I have incredible enthusiasm and will become an asset to this business." What a bright eyed, bushy tailed, young little whipper snipper. I was only eighteen, but I knew I was worth more than what I was currently being paid, so I persisted. Eventually my persistence paid off and I was offered a full-time position, Monday to Friday, at a business bar in Sydney's CBD. It wasn't long before I also started working weekends at one of the company's nightclubs and so began my savings to travel the world.

Two years later is when my best friend and I headed off to Europe for that working holiday. We had only planned a couple of weeks in Thailand to relax followed by three months working in the Greek Islands, then three months working in Spain. Little did we know we would be gone for more than eighteen months in total and see many more countries than we had originally anticipated. We worked our way through bars and restaurants throughout Europe having the time of our lives, yet the pressure of society's expectations always plagued the back of my mind, which is why after eighteen months I headed home. I was sweating the small stuff. Big time. What was I doing with my life? Here I was, living in Europe, working without a visa at twenty-one and didn't even have my driver's license. My current self would tell my younger self "Who cares baby, you have all the time in the world for that small stuff." Yet I felt a strong urge to go home and "sort out my life" based on societal norms, so I left my best friends and came home.

When I arrived my brother kindly offered me a role as his personal assistant at his construction company. I also got a weekend job again at the bar I previously worked at in the city and started studying a course one night a week in "The Principles and Elements of Design." I was hoping to potentially become an interior designer. I had such a passion for creativity and just loved decorating friends' and families' houses or rooms, so I thought this would be right up my alley. It wasn't long before I told my brother that I had to quit working for him before I ended up hating him (so he often reminds me) as he was a tough boss and I was a real softy. I had been offered a job at a local surf shop chain so then it was back to retail for me. After a year I applied for a data entry role at a surf label and was doing my whole pitch again, "Even though I have no experience, I know I have incredible enthusiasm and will become an asset to this business." The Sales Manager saw right through me and said "Honey, you aren't a data entry kind of person, you are a sales-person. There is no point in trying to fit a square peg into a round hole." I got the job anyway and was quite impressed with myself. As it turned out, the Sales Manager was right.

Returning home after Canada and South America, I found a job selling radio and television advertising. Man, if I thought retail was cut throat, I had another thing coming! This industry was next level but this epic lesson helped me to build an understanding of the world of business, what I was good at, and how to manage an independent workload. I spent two years working for this company learning so much about myself, autonomy, the industry itself, and discovered that I was much better at building long term relationships than this burn and churn of low-end advertising. I applied for an account manager role at another business and landed the position, which I held for the following few years. Looking back over the decade of my twenties, some might say I was a lost little girl jumping from one industry to another around the world. Others might say I was just doing what young people do and experiencing life. The point is, it doesn't really matter what anybody else had to say about the life I was living, let alone anyone's opinion on the life YOU choose to live. It is YOUR life, they are YOUR experiences to have, YOUR dots to connect and when YOU get to the end of it all YOU want to be able to look back and think that YOU got to experience everything that YOUR heart desired by pursuing what YOU loved, not someone else's perception of how your life or life in general should be lived. Your experiences are perfectly orchestrated to guide you on your unique path for your unique journey here on earth. You are responsible for reminding yourself that you are OK and the universe has your back.

One of my favourite, most influential people of all time made a speech about that exact point at Stanford University in 2005. Steve Jobs. He said, "Today I want to tell you three stories from my life. That's it. No big deal. Just three stories." His first story was about connecting the dots. He talked to the graduates about dropping out of Reed College so he could "drop in" to the courses he wanted to take, like calligraphy, a course that had no practical application to his life. Ten years on he incorporated what he had previously learned into the design of the Macintosh Computer. "It was the first computer with beautiful typography... You can't connect the dots looking forward; you can only connect them looking backwards. You have to trust the dots will somehow connect in your future. You have to trust in something—your gut, destiny, life, karma, whatever. This approach has never let me down and it has made all the difference in my life."

Steve's second story was about love and loss. He recalled falling in love with computers at an early age, meeting "Woz" (Steve Wozniak), building Apple from his parents' garage, and losing Apple after a falling out with the Board of Directors. "Getting fired was the best thing that could ever have happened to me... I'm convinced that the only thing that kept me going was that I loved what I did. You've got to find what you love." You see, you may not know it in the present moment but what you are going through right now is preparing you exactly for what is to come.

Steve's third story was about the finality of death. "Remembering that are you going to die is the best way I know to avoid the trap thinking you have something to lose. You are already naked. There is no reason not to follow your heart." Pretty potent stuff, right? We are all here for a limited amount of time. This is your life, your love, and your choice what you want to do with it all and that is why this chapter is more of a working chapter than a reading chapter, so get the pen out and let's define this with CONVICTION!

Have you ever sat down and really asked yourself the hard-hitting questions? All BS aside, not one single external contributing factor, just you, your ultimate dream life, perfect day from start to finish and written down your answers? I mean you might daydream about these from time to time, but now we all know the power of writing things down, don't you think it's time we took that next step? We are all either cruising through life consciously seeking or consciously sleeping. That's what I think, and that can all change profoundly NOW in this here present moment we share together. It is not by chance you are reading this book. Like I said earlier, it is by choice. You have a deep yearning for change. That's why you are here, and I am here to try to help you implement that change as best as I can through the pages of this book and these exercises involving the tools of empowerment and activation that helped me personally. The rest is quite poetically up to you.

So here are some categories and questions as guidelines to draw your attention to what you love, who you want to be, how you want to be and how you can go about getting there. This is a killer tool of empowerment to use as your true north for all decision-making beyond today. If you find yourself questioning whether or not you should go ahead with a particular opportunity in your life, moving to a new house, changing jobs, business ventures, holidays, studying etc., refer to your questions and answers below and ask yourself;

- Does this align with what I know I want?
- Will this help get me to get to where I need to go?
- Do I need to re-evaluate this situation?

Let's get started on your Introverted Excavation Self Enquiry and remember this, your "WHY" is the most powerful and commanding rocket fuel for all of your answers so, be very specific and brutally honest with yourself. This component is the real game changer with questions to help guide you back to your divine true knowing.

86

To be yourself IN A WORLD THAT IS CONSTANTLY TRYING TO MAKE YOU SOMETHING ELSE IS THE GREATEST Accomplishment

RALPH WALDO EMERSON SAID THAT

Holistic Human Activation #4

Introverted Excavator

Category 1—Holistic Health

Let's start with this powerful and profound category as quite often this aspect can have a wicked domino effect on all other categories in your life. Now if you are anything like me and you hate writing in books and would prefer to write this on a worksheet, feel free to head over to www.courtneystarchild.com/universe for a print out of the following life shaping activity.

THE INTROVERTED EXCAVATOR SELF ENQUIRY
Category ONE - Holistic Health

My biggest goal in this category is:

_____

_____

_____

	Strongly Agree	Agree	Somewhat Agree	Disagree	Strongly Disagree
I consciously choose to love my body	☐	☐	☐	☐	☐
I support balance in my body enjoying a wide variety of predominantly plant based foods and more	☐	☐	☐	☐	☐
I understand the importance of whole food nutrition support in my body for healing, immunity & vitality	☐	☐	☐	☐	☐
I have educated myself regarding health & nutrition	☐	☐	☐	☐	☐
I drink 1L to every 10kg of my body weight every day	☐	☐	☐	☐	☐
I have regular health check ups with the doctor & the dentist	☐	☐	☐	☐	☐
I invest in my health	☐	☐	☐	☐	☐
I have a clearly defined fitness regime that I am committed to	☐	☐	☐	☐	☐
I am incredibly grateful for my body and its ability to heal and regenerate	☐	☐	☐	☐	☐
I have thought deeply about my health and know what I want in this category of my life	☐	☐	☐	☐	☐

THE INTROVERTED EXCAVATOR SELF ENQUIRY

Category two - Mastering Your Mind

My biggest goal in this category is:

_ _

_ _

_ _

	Strongly Agree	Agree	Somewhat Agree	Disagree	Strongly Disagree
I commit to stilling my mind at least once a day	☐	☐	☐	☐	☐
I understand the benefits, power & importance of stilling my mind daily for overall mental health	☐	☐	☐	☐	☐
I give gratitude daily	☐	☐	☐	☐	☐
I have a consistently positive attitude towards life	☐	☐	☐	☐	☐
I feel confident in my intellectual abilities	☐	☐	☐	☐	☐
I understand the power of change right now is within me	☐	☐	☐	☐	☐
I am committed to a self care ritual	☐	☐	☐	☐	☐
I am consciously aware of my thoughts and their power	☐	☐	☐	☐	☐
I prioritize expanding my mind regularly through culture, reading & learning	☐	☐	☐	☐	☐
I have thought deeply about my mindset & know what I want in this category of my life	☐	☐	☐	☐	☐

THE INTROVERTED EXCAVATOR SELF ENQUIRY

Category THREE – Emotional Education

My biggest goal in this category is:

_ _

_ _

_ _

	Strongly Agree	Agree	Somewhat Agree	Disagree	Strongly Disagree
I can articulate a wide variety of emotions	☐	☐	☐	☐	☐
I can articulate & define specific emotions that are of importance to me	☐	☐	☐	☐	☐
I am aware of emotions that require my efforts	☐	☐	☐	☐	☐
I can identify emotions I experience when I am emotionally engaged	☐	☐	☐	☐	☐
I can acknowledge when I am emotionally triggered & interrupt the process to self regulate	☐	☐	☐	☐	☐
I am aware of my core values	☐	☐	☐	☐	☐
I am committed to a self care ritual	☐	☐	☐	☐	☐
I have the ability to acknowledge when I am emotionally triggered and interrupt the process to self regulate	☐	☐	☐	☐	☐
I prioritise personal development to enhance my life & expand my mind	☐	☐	☐	☐	☐
I have thought deeply about my emotions & know what I want in this category of my life	☐	☐	☐	☐	☐

THE INTROVERTED EXCAVATOR SELF ENQUIRY
Category FOUR – Charisma of Character

My biggest goal in this category is:

_ _
_ _
_ _

	Strongly Agree	Agree	Somewhat Agree	Disagree	Strongly Disagree
I have a positive relationship with my mother	☐	☐	☐	☐	☐
I have a positive relationship with my father	☐	☐	☐	☐	☐
I have positive relationships with my siblings	☐	☐	☐	☐	☐
I have a positive relationship with myself	☐	☐	☐	☐	☐
I know who I am and what I want from life	☐	☐	☐	☐	☐
I put effort into relationships that nourish me	☐	☐	☐	☐	☐
I am aware of relationships that drain me	☐	☐	☐	☐	☐
I feel confident to decide the direction of my life	☐	☐	☐	☐	☐
I have confidence & believe in myself	☐	☐	☐	☐	☐
I have thought deeply about my character & know what I want in this category of my life	☐	☐	☐	☐	☐

THE INTROVERTED EXCAVATOR SELF ENQUIRY
Category FIVE - Spiritual Satisfaction

My biggest goal in this category is:

_____

_____

_____

	Strongly Agree	Agree	Somewhat Agree	Disagree	Strongly Disagree
I can clearly define & articulate my spiritual beliefs	☐	☐	☐	☐	☐
I feel very fulfilled as a human being	☐	☐	☐	☐	☐
I am committed daily to my spiritual practice	☐	☐	☐	☐	☐
I live very consciously & pay attention to all areas of my life	☐	☐	☐	☐	☐
I contribute to others & make the world a better place	☐	☐	☐	☐	☐
I am accepting of all parts of myself, physically, mentally & emotionally	☐	☐	☐	☐	☐
I am forgiving of all parts of myself, physically, mentally, emotionally	☐	☐	☐	☐	☐
I am loving to all parts of myself, physically, mentally, emotionally	☐	☐	☐	☐	☐
I am very content most of the time	☐	☐	☐	☐	☐
I have thought deeply about my spirituality & know what I want in this category of my life	☐	☐	☐	☐	☐

THE INTROVERTED EXCAVATOR SELF ENQUIRY

Category SIX - Love & Intimacy

My biggest goal in this category is:

- -
- -
- -

	Strongly Agree	Agree	Somewhat Agree	Disagree	Strongly Disagree
I am in a fantastic & loving relationship	☐	☐	☐	☐	☐
I would say our relationship is passionate	☐	☐	☐	☐	☐
We have plenty of quality alone time set aside	☐	☐	☐	☐	☐
We have a very fulfilling sex life	☐	☐	☐	☐	☐
I have focused an appropriate amount of energy on my partners needs	☐	☐	☐	☐	☐
Our relaionship is exciting	☐	☐	☐	☐	☐
We communicate easily, openly & honestly	☐	☐	☐	☐	☐
I rarely experience stress in my love relationship	☐	☐	☐	☐	☐
I consider myself to be a very good partner in my relationship	☐	☐	☐	☐	☐
I have thought deeply about love & intimacy & know what I want in this category of my life	☐	☐	☐	☐	☐

THE INTROVERTED EXCAVATOR SELF ENQUIRY

Category SEVEN – Luscious Leadership

My biggest goal in this category is:

_____
_____
_____

	Strongly Agree	Agree	Somewhat Agree	Disagree	Strongly Disagree
I know I am deserving of happiness	☐	☐	☐	☐	☐
I can define appropriate boundaries in my life	☐	☐	☐	☐	☐
I have a strong sense of how I would like my life to unfold over the coming years	☐	☐	☐	☐	☐
I have a protege/child/children	☐	☐	☐	☐	☐
I have a loving relationship with my children/protege	☐	☐	☐	☐	☐
I focus quality time with each of my children/ protege every week	☐	☐	☐	☐	☐
I set a great example to my children/protege how to live a wonderful life	☐	☐	☐	☐	☐
I rarely experience anxiety with my children/protege	☐	☐	☐	☐	☐
Overall I feel I am an exemplary role model	☐	☐	☐	☐	☐
I have thought deeply about leadership & know what I want in this category of my life	☐	☐	☐	☐	☐

95

THE INTROVERTED EXCAVATOR SELF ENQUIRY
Category EIGHT - Savvy Social Life

My biggest goal in this category is:

_ _

_ _

_ _

	Strongly Agree	Agree	Somewhat Agree	Disagree	Strongly Disagree
I have a fantastic active social life	☐	☐	☐	☐	☐
I am happy with the friendships in my life	☐	☐	☐	☐	☐
I have many positive friendships in my life	☐	☐	☐	☐	☐
I make an effort to make new friendships	☐	☐	☐	☐	☐
I know my vibe attracts my tribe	☐	☐	☐	☐	☐
My friends have positive behaviours	☐	☐	☐	☐	☐
My friends inspire me	☐	☐	☐	☐	☐
I make an effort each week to connect with friends	☐	☐	☐	☐	☐
I know who I am and what I want from my friendships	☐	☐	☐	☐	☐
I have thought deeply about my social life & know what I want in this category of my life	☐	☐	☐	☐	☐

THE INTROVERTED EXCAVATOR SELF ENQUIRY
Category NINE – Wild Abundance

My biggest goal in this category is:

_____
_____
_____

	Strongly Agree	Agree	Somewhat Agree	Disagree	Strongly Disagree
I am passionate about many things in my life	☐	☐	☐	☐	☐
I manage my finances well	☐	☐	☐	☐	☐
I have clearly defined & written financial goals	☐	☐	☐	☐	☐
I understand the fundamentals of wealth creation	☐	☐	☐	☐	☐
I love the house I live in	☐	☐	☐	☐	☐
I have a lot of fun in my life	☐	☐	☐	☐	☐
I have regular travel holidays	☐	☐	☐	☐	☐
I plan extraordinary experiences for myself regularly	☐	☐	☐	☐	☐
Making money & creating wealth are good things	☐	☐	☐	☐	☐
I have thought deeply about abundance & know what I want in this category of my life	☐	☐	☐	☐	☐

THE INTROVERTED EXCAVATOR SELF ENQUIRY

Category TEN – Lifetime Legacy

My biggest goal in this category is:

_ _
_ _
_ _

	Strongly Agree	Agree	Somewhat Agree	Disagree	Strongly Disagree
I am dedicated to improving my life in all categories	☐	☐	☐	☐	☐
I currently have a plan in place for achieving my ideal life	☐	☐	☐	☐	☐
I currently use tools of empowerment to help me achieve my ultimate life	☐	☐	☐	☐	☐
I love what I do - my career is very fulfilling to me	☐	☐	☐	☐	☐
I look forward to my work day frequently	☐	☐	☐	☐	☐
I can clearly define my single most important goal	☐	☐	☐	☐	☐
I know how I want to contribute to the community at large	☐	☐	☐	☐	☐
I feel connected to the universe at large	☐	☐	☐	☐	☐
I am happy with what I have made with myself in my life	☐	☐	☐	☐	☐
I have thought deeply about my lifetime legacy & know what I want in this category of my life	☐	☐	☐	☐	☐

The bottom line with discovering who you truly are is really asking yourself the hard hitting questions to discover what you think and how you really feel in all different areas of your life. Its not always pretty but owning your story and allowing your MESS to become your MESSAGE is one of THE most powerfully liberating ways to live your life.

At this stage you should have at least practiced the Monkey Mind Meditation and have an idea of how it resonates with you. Some people like it and some people don't, like many things in life. It is imperative you find a meditation styles that best suits you and YOUR mind. I love this one because there are so many elements and my mind is so active, for me it is much easier to slow the mind down when I am focusing on multiple aspects of a meditation such as visualisation, mantra AND mudra. In saying that, you might be the exact opposite of me, have a more relaxed natural thought pattern and prefer to sit quietly without mantra. If that is you, I invite you to try the below meditation instead or alternate. I will give you a few different meditations to experiment with throughout this book so hopefully; by the final page you will have found one that deeply resonates with you to carry on into your future. Meditation is the key to complete happiness, contentment and liberation in life, so you'd best find a key that fits for you.

Meditating On The White Light

Posture

In any comfortable position with the spine straight

Eyes

Closed and focused at the third eye point

Mudra

Hands rested comfortably on the knees

Visualisation

As you inhale a nice slow, long, deep breath through the nostrils with your eyes closed, I want you to visualise a bright white light coming up your spine through your seat, imagining this bright white light washing over every piece of your body, both inside and out as it rises though your entire being, as you exhale a nice long deep breath through your nose I want you to imagine drawing the healing white light energy down through your body, down the spine and back out through the seat of your body into the earth, then back up again along the spine, through the crown, down the spine and back to the earth and so on. Repeat this exercise for at least 5 minutes.

Duration

Do yourself a solid and set an alarm so you can get totally lost in the breath. In your own time work up from 5 minutes to 11 minutes then 21 minutes. Enjoy.

Scientific Benefits

- Unlocks your natural healing capacity and increases your overall wellbeing
- Improves Self Confidence
- Helps to clear painful emotions
- Strengthens your own energetic field
- Purifies your energy centres
- Activates your will force
- Cleanses grosser toxic energies from the physical system
- Protects you from the influence of negative energies

Rehash

⭐ Remind yourself;

⭐ I am ok

⭐ I know where I am going

⭐ I know who I am

⭐ I am committed

⭐ I won't sweat the small stuff

⭐ MEDITATE

⭐ Share your story, journey, experiences, breakdowns and breakthroughs with each other on the Rocking Rock Bottom FB Page

KNOWING WHO YOU ARE

Is the greatest wisdom

A HUMAN BEING

CAN POSSESS

KNOW YOUR GOALS

WHAT YOU LOVE

YOUR MORALS YOUR NEEDS

YOUR STANDARDS

WHAT YOU WILL NOT TOLERATE &

What you are willing to die for

IT DEFINES WHO YOU ARE

BEYONCE SAID THAT

CHAPTER 5

Rocking Your Story Like a Rock Star

Accepting Who You Are And Owning That Sh**

It's a lot easier said than done because we don't always like where we have come from, what we have done or who we have become in the process. The funny thing is though, people are a lot more accepting, compassionate and forgiving towards you when you are open, honest and vulnerable with your truth. It takes some extreme courage to own your mistakes, to stand up in the face of adversity and acknowledge your poor behaviours, learn from the experience and pivot towards the person you want to be or the person you want to become. Brene Brown says, "When we deny the story, it defines us. When we own the story we can write a brave new ending." So we need to empower ourselves into more than just self-acceptance. We need to empower ourselves into Rocking Our Stories Like Rock Stars!

As I sit here in a beautiful café in Palm Beach, overlooking the sea, the cool ocean breeze dancing through my hair, I reflect on a time five years ago when I had just called off my wedding to Josh. It was one of the most emotionally crushing, confusing, difficult and lonely times of my adult life. From the moment we met we were a force to be reckoned with. It was back in 2010 at The Gold Coast Turf Club, and although I'm not really one for the racetrack, my Aunty had won four free tickets to the members stand on a local radio station, so we decided to go. I had invited a friend to join my Aunt, my mum and myself, however she pulled out at the last minute, so it was just us "Three Musketeers." We always seemed to get up to mischief when the three of us got together and this day was nothing shy of that. We were dressed for success and ready to rumble. We headed up to the members' stand and got ourselves a nice bottle of wine. The atmosphere was meek, somber and boring' to be frank. As we looked out through the glass windows, the day was glorious, sun bellowing down on the punters below, a sea of men and women basking in the sunshine while we were tucked away in this small, air-conditioned glass box. It wasn't long before I had convinced my entourage to head down to the general admission area to join in the festivities. As we entered the huge sea of humans, we were receiving a lot of attention. We made our way over to the bar to line up for a bottle of wine when a young man tapped me on the shoulder. I turned around to see a young, confident, strawberry blonde man, like Matthew Mc Conaughey in "Dazed and Confused" oozing with swagger, standing behind me.

"Are you married?" he asked.

"No," I replied.

Joshua Charles Coghlan—The love of my life 2010—A man of incredible swagger, charisma and incessant annoyingness.

"Do you want to be?"

Hahahahahahaha.

Seriously, the audacity of this young fella. Still to this day that one liner cracks me up. His sense of humor caught my attention without a question of a doubt. That bold, brazen young man going fiercely after what he wanted. I liked that. And I liked that what he wanted was me. We proceeded to chat until the ladies had finished their wine and wanted to return to the members' area. Lucky for Josh we had a spare ticket and my Aunty kindly obliged by letting him join us in return for his purchase of a bottle of wine. The rest is history.

Two years later we were living in Freshwater on Sydney's Northern Beaches. I had been out of town for work and was heading home a few hours early to surprise Josh before we were supposed to be going out for dinner. I was a bit tired so wanted to reschedule but Josh insisted on us going out, so we stuck with the original plans. As I walked in the front door two hours ahead of schedule, a surprised Josh was caught red handed packing away a bunch of tea light candles. He claimed he was "cleaning up" after our room-mate, however Josh was definitely not known for cleaning up after himself, let alone one of our house mates, so I was pretty suspicious as to what he had been up to whilst I was out of town. I went for a run while he finished "cleaning up" and returned home to get dressed for dinner. We had a magical night out at Whale Beach as he wined and dined me at a very fancy restaurant, the service was impeccable, my cheeks so sore from smiling and laughing all night long and when we returned home there were rose petals and tea light candles everywhere leading from the front gate to our bedroom where our song "Madness" by Muse was playing. He had organised for our roommate to set this all up whilst we were out at dinner and had been pre-burning the wicks to make lighting the tea light candles easier for our roomie. There was a box of goodies for me to open, and I still, at this point had no idea what was about to happen. My favourite candle from Glass House, my fave perfume, some saucy lingerie... oh this guy was gearing up for some sweet sweet loving I thought, and then there was a letter. I opened it up and my eyes shot straight to the bottom line on the page immediately. Will you marry me?

Time stood still.

This was it.

Josh was proposing to me.

I couldn't believe it.

I didn't want to take my eyes off the page, so I drank in the scene through my peripheral, etching it into my memory bank. After reading the whole page and arriving back at "Will you marry me?"

I looked up and he was on one knee with a ring box in his hand. I went over, sat on his knee and kissed him. He then asked,

"Does that mean yes?"

We both laughed.

"Yes it does"

We then called all our parents to share the exciting news.

It was three years after this, we were living on the Gold Coast and had a huge fight so I packed my bags and left, never to return again. A few weeks after that I moved back to Sydney by myself and at that time my brother had a windows business. He once again gave me a job as his personal assistant. I spent my whole workweek in a concrete box of an office without any windows, which was quite ironic seeing as I was working for a windows company. The isolation and loneliness was killing me. Meg Mac "Roll Up Your Sleeves" and The Preatures "Two Tone Melody" were the soundtracks to my heartache. I remember driving on the highway one day thinking "I can't cope" and a huge red flag went up in my mind. I had been through some crazy challenging times in my life, but never, I mean NEVER had I felt or thought those three words. It was time to get help. So I went to the doctors and got a referral for a psychologist. I'm so glad that I never had any stigma around this kind of thing, and I deeply encourage anyone working through incredibly challenging emotional times to have the courage to seek help. You are stronger than you know and you just need to understand how to get curious about your emotions and how best to manage them with tools. These people are trained in the psychology of the mind and know the tools to use to break challenges down into bite size pieces and overcome the habits and patterns we aren't consciously aware of. My first three sessions were pretty teary to be honest. They were all about my childhood, my family, my broken relationship and me. One day my therapist, Tara, handed me a piece of paper with eighteen symptoms outlined on it and asked me to identify if I had experienced any. Fourteen of the eighteen I circled. I also learned that one of the reasons I like to keep such a tidy home is because if there is chaos in my home, much like the chaos of my childhood, then I struggle to relax. Things were making a lot of sense to me now. Tara explained to me that what I had been experiencing was in fact emotional trauma and she helped me to learn how to better articulate myself and my emotions in times of distress.

Situation Outline the situation.

Feeling Identify my feelings.

Need Articulate what I need in this type of situation moving forward.

What I learned through this process was that my old coping mechanisms were no longer working. When I was emotionally flooded my knee jerk response was "flight-mode" and I would act in haste, in the heat of the moment and run. Just like we did when I was growing up. At one session we discussed what it was that I wanted for my future. It was to have a family, build a successful business, marry Josh and for us to never fight. Tara reassured me that these were all very real and achievable goals, except of course for the not fighting part. "All couples fight, you just need to learn to do it effectively," she said. From then on Josh and I started to talk on the phone again and he began flying down to Sydney to visit me every other weekend. It wasn't long before we decided to "officially" work things out, discussed how we both wanted to start a family and there was no time like the present. We had that discussion and I immediately fell pregnant. I landed a transfer with work and within months moved back to Queensland. Right now was the biggest challenge of all, facing up to everyone I left behind after cutting and running earlier in the year. I had to own my sh**, rock it like a Rock Star and let go of the past, live here in the present and forgive myself for the choices I made and the pain I caused myself and the people I left behind. We all did. I had to look at all of my lessons as blessings to grow into the woman I was here to become. Cynthia Occelli once said, "For a seed to achieve its greatest expression, it must come completely undone. The shell cracks, its insides come out and everything changes. To someone who doesn't understand growth, it would look like complete destruction." Sometimes we need to reach that point. The point of no return. The point of complete destruction so we can reshape, readjust, realign and reset our lives. If we aren't in an uncomfortable place, we aren't likely to move, so sometimes the universe makes things so uncomfortable for us that we have no other choice but to take affirmative action. And so, we move.

Still to this day, subconscious beliefs and unconscious neurological programs in my mind are a huge work in progress for me. Last year, after the universe had been putting The Emotional Freedom Technique in front of me, from the time I was in hospital to the time I did the Gabby Bernstein Master Class, I decided I was going to finally bite the bullet and check out this so called "Tapping" technique. I found a course, enrolled and totally went and blew my mind with the power of this incredibly simple, yet profound and proven tool for rewiring the subconscious mind.

We were asked to remember anything between the age of zero to seven, as irrelevant or insignificant as it may seem because as adults these experiences may seem laughable as we now have the wisdom and strategies to dismiss such ridiculous situations, however these tiny traumas are the ones that can have a huge impact on shaping our little people's beliefs in themselves and the world around them.

To master
YOUR DESTINY
You must
EMBRACE
Your history

WHO KNOWS WHO SAID THAT BUT TRUTH BOMB ALERT

So we had to recall whatever just popped into our mind, and not a big trauma, a little one. I had LOADS of big doozeys but couldn't quite remember a little one, and then out of the depths of my childhood memories popped an insignificant situation of a time when a boy at school yelled out "Courtney Crusaders, home-made Potaters". Now let me set the scene for you. This kid was not a kid I often interacted with, acknowledged, liked, looked up to, admired, noticed or really cared about. He was just another kid on the playground and indifferent to me. He had big ears that stuck out like saucers and glasses as thick as thimbles. Stereotypically he was a geeky looking boy that had the brass "you know what's" to be picking on little old me, an innocent young girl seeking everyone's admiration and approval. The lady conducting the training, Caroline, is an absolute master at what she does. I've personally dubbed her "The Queen of Coincidences," because once you start working on clearing these "Energetic Consciousness Holograms" or as they officially call them, "ECHOs", you start experiencing coincidences. So seeing as Caroline helps you clear your energetic blocks and creates these coincidences, she is The Queen of them as far as I am concerned. When I was doing the training in October 2018, she asked me to recall what I thought and felt at that time, as six-year-old Courtney. I felt embarrassed. I felt rejected. I felt ugly. Why? Because whilst all the little girls at that age were playing with Slinky's, the boys were playing with these Crusaders, ugly, green, wart covered monsters, like Quasimodo. To little Courtney, this kid was professing in front of all of the other kids on the playground that I was a disgusting, ugly monster. As an adult I would simply shrug this off and think, "Get stuffed buddy, I'm awesome." But as a little babe, I was devastated. We went through the process of tapping until the feelings dissipated. Caroline explained that usually when an event has been cleared from your energetic field you would receive a confirmation from the universe.

After this session we had a lunch break and one of my fellow class participants, Deb, and I were sitting eating lunch at a café nearby when a stranger came over, excused herself for interrupting and said, "I just had to stop to tell you how beautiful you are. I walked past you earlier and just had to tell you when I came back past." Confirmation. Thank you Universe. I was a little embarrassed at the time to admit such a superficial comment had made such a big impact on my subconscious beliefs, but after experiencing the teachings, the tools and the confirmation, I knew I had found a life-altering tool that I had to share with everyone and anyone.

Beauty begins

THE MOMENT
YOU DECIDE
TO BE

Yourself

COCO CHANEL SAID THAT

It was in 1944 that a man named Max Planck, the man many consider the father of quantum theory, shocked the world by saying there is a "Matrix" of energy that provides the blueprint for our physical world. In this place of pure energy everything begins, from the birth of stars, DNA, to our deepest relationships, peace between nations to our very own personal healing. This place of pure energy is the place you viscerally experience when you drop into shuniya (definition—zero, nothing, openness). The point of stillness or pure connectedness when we become one with the all-encompassing energy of the universe. LOVE.

Gregg Braden, five times New York Times Best Selling Author of Consciousness Literature explains that there is a field of energy that connect everything. The field plays the role of container and mirror for our beliefs. The field is holographic. Every part is connected to every other. The Matrix is another name for what quantum physicists call the quantum field. Imprinting is what refers to the system by which humans take on the characteristics of their parents by observation and imitation. So EFT Tapping rewires the neurological subconscious patterns in the mind and Martix Re-Imprinting changes the images in our "hologram" or deep seated memory and that is what creates our foundational belief systems from the age of 0–6 years old.

Subconscious programs run 95-99% of our daily behavior, activities and habits. Many of these negative programs were imprinted in the first six years of your life as I outlined in my personal story above, and they are based on trauma, misperceptions and observing those around you. These programs are based on images of past events, held in your local fields and regarded subconsciously as current events. Eventually when these negative programs erode your coping mechanisms and cause enough stress, the body will try to adapt at a chemical, hormonal, cellular and DNA level. As this continues to happen and trigger these chemical and/or hormonal reactions, you eventually come to develop physical or psychological "dis-ease". Matrix Re-Imprinting changes these images and the replacement of these images creates a permanent healing effect. The whole subject absolutely fascinated me throughout the course as I watched demonstration after demonstration of people who had been living in suffering for so long, finally transform their minds and go on to transform their lives.

From the time I decided I wanted to write my book about my experiences in hospital and having been meditating daily since, I was experiencing visions and ideas around creating an event called "The Self-Empowerment Movement". When I completed the EFT and Matrix Re-imprinting course, I asked Caroline if she would be interested in sharing her Self-Empowerment Tool of Tapping & Matrix Re-Imprinting at the event. She kindly accepted the invitation. I was thrilled. After nine months of no contact between us, I had an urge to reach out to see if she was still interested to join me. It had been so long since we had spoken, and I was in the process of approaching other speakers for the event, so I reached out. "Coincidentally" she happened to be on the Gold Coast that very weekend from Victoria where she usually lives so we arranged to meet to discuss details in depth. We got together a few nights later and had a fabulous time catching up talking about what each of us had been working on and life in general. I was discussing the joys of parenthood and how I liked things better in my relationship with Josh when we were "in the trenches" together. Caroline picked up on that expression right away and said, "That's not an expression used very often, I think that might be a past life thing." Now I'm not sure about your perspective about "past life experiences" but to me, anyone could make up any story, tell you whatever they like and how are you supposed to know or reference it as real or not? Exactly. If you were to go and see a Psychic and they told you about experiences you have had in your life of loved ones you have lost, you can absolutely vouch for that as being real or absurd. So, when Caroline said this, I was curious but also cautious with how I perceive that type of thing. We discussed meeting up again in a week in Brisbane. This time we did a session and started with my self-belief. In the process of writing this book and organising this monumental event, a lot of thoughts like this were coming up;

"Who am I to write a book?"
"Who am I to host an event?"
"Who would want to come to one of my events anyway?"

From all of the personal development work I had been doing I was very well aware of these thoughts, consciously trying not to attach to them and keep moving forward towards what I was trying to create. As our session progressed and we went from one ECHO (Emotional Consciousness Hologram) to the next, about three in, Caroline said "Ok, now we are going to work on this past life stuff with Josh. Are you ready?" She repeated the phrase "In the trenches" and asked if anything popped into mind when she said that. A still, sepia tone image popped into mind, much like this one on the following page that I found online afterwards.

Now history knowledge isn't a strength of mine so at the time, to me, it was two ANZAC's (for those who don't know what that means—Australian & New Zealand Army Corps) Soldiers in a trench, but I knew the hats were like these ones pictured, so it must have been from WWI. Anyway, from here we explored what feelings came up when I concentrated on this picture in my mind; there were feelings of strong friendship, respon-sibility, loss and grief. It felt like two best friends went away to war together and only one came home. They were supposed to be the best of friends for life and watch each other have families whilst living on the same street. That kind of feeling.

Photo Courtesy of <u>tes.com</u> *Lesson World War 1 Trench Warfare*

I didn't consciously know where this was all coming from, but I could feel what I was feeling and that is what we were working on—clearing, the grief and responsibility for maybe coming home alone without my so-called best friend for life. The energy was cleared until there was no charge left and we wrapped up for the afternoon. The next morning, I woke up and whilst I was getting the children's breakfast ready, I thought I would turn on Netflix. What I like about Netflix for my kids is that I get to choose what they watch and there are no commercials luring them to buy this toy or that cereal. Unfortunately, that morning, Netflix just would not work so I switched over to Free To Air TV and Sunrise was on, into the kitchen I went to finish preparing breakfast. As I was listening to Kochi, he was reporting how Woolworths and Coles were using Ooshies and Little Shop Collectables, fighting "IN THE TRENCHES" for your grocery dollars! I couldn't believe my ears! The coincidences were just so on point, so impeccably timed and come on, what are the chances Netflix doesn't work, Free To Air comes on and Kochi says "In the trenches". Seriously???

MIND BLOWN.

Sometimes the idea of changing our conscious belief systems is extremely overwhelming let alone our subconscious ones which is why this here tool is one of the greatest gifts of ALL TIME!

Holistic Human Activation #5

EFT Tapping

Re-wiring your subconscious limiting belief systems is one of the most liberating exercises you can do to completely overhaul your life. This can be done through "Matrix Re-imprinting" which is a tool you can learn at a course with a trained practitioner, however "EFT" tapping is a tool that we can get you started with immediately, right now in the comfort of your own space. This can help you with food cravings, addictions, alcohol and cigarettes, limiting sub conscious belief systems. EVERYTHING AND ANYTHING! Some of the world's greatest athletes have used these techniques to better their performances and overcome their own limiting self-beliefs, that's how tremendously powerful this stuff is! It is one of the most non-invasive, gentle yet profound tools of empowerment and is the one that is going to build up your bulletproof, badass self. It's weird, it's simple and boy, oh boy does it work. Below outlined are the most common limiting self-beliefs that everybody experiences. Identify which one is a strong stand out for you and start there. You can head over to www.courtneystarchild.com/universe for tapping demonstrations, scripts and courses to get you going on your way to ROCKING YOUR STORY LIKE A ROCKSTAR!

Common Limiting Self Beliefs

Im unlovable

I can't do it

People are out to get me

Im flawed

Im not capable

It's not fair

Im insignificant

Im bad

Im unforgivable

People must think well of me

Something bad will happen

People take advantage of me

Im guilty

Im a failure

Im worthless

Im misunderstood

Im unattractive

Im powerless

Im abandoned

Im alone

Im sinful

Im dumb

Im a victim

The world is a dangerous place

Im helpless

Life is hopeless

I must be perfect to be loved

I must be in control

People are over sensitive

Im not good enough

I don't deserve it

Im not worthy

It'll never happen to me

I've lost control

Im unproductive

I get stood on

Im sensitive

Im used

Im trapped

Im inferior

Im betrayed

Im vulnerable

Im un-teachable

Im confused

Resolver Meditation

Posture

Sit comfortably with a straight spine and a slight neck lock.

Eyes

Close the eyes 9/10ths of the way.

Mudra

Place the hands over the chest, with the palms on the torso, at the level of the breasts. The fingers point towards each other across the chest.

Breath

The key to this meditation is attention to the breath.

Inhale deeply and completely for 5 seconds.

Exhale completely for 5 seconds.

Hold the breath out for 15 seconds.

By suspending the chest motion as you pull in the navel point and abdomen.

Duration

Begin with 11 minutes. Build up to 31 or 62 minutes.

To End

Inhale deeply and stretch the arms up over the head. Relax the breath and shake the arms and hands for 15-30 seconds. Relax.

Scientific Benefits

This is a form of ancient humanological therapy. We are often confused and held in deadlock when inner conflict blocks our ability to think and act clearly. In these moments the mind's prana (its primary energy or vital force) is scattered and distributed in a disturbed manner. This breath pattern holds the breath out three times as long as it is held in. So, the body senses a lack of prana in vital areas of functioning and asks how it can quickly and optimally reorganise itself to respond to this survival threat. The fibers of the Pranic Body extend and re-channel the prana to form a new pattern filled with clarity and action potential. Your built-in computer can calculate your total resources and the level of challenge, then design a strategy to prepare and use the mind and body effectively. This meditation resolves many conflicts and is an automatic reflex for survival. Inner conflict is the result of excess or disturbed prana. The effect is certain, gradual and simple. Be honest with the breath timing and the meditation will be honest with you.

Rehash

- ⭐ Situation—Feeling—Need

- ⭐ Don't attach to negative thoughts

- ⭐ Identify your limiting belief

- ⭐ Give gratitude for its lessons so far

- ⭐ EFT TAPPING—tap tap taperoo

- ⭐ Oh yeah and MEDITATE

- ⭐ Share your story, journey, experiences, breakdowns and breakthroughs with each other on the Rocking Rock Bottom FB Page

When we deny

THE STORY

IT DEFINES US

WHEN WE OWN

THE STORY

WE CAN WRITE

A brave new ending

BRENE BROWN SAID THAT

CHAPTER 6

Harmonising Your Health Becoming Superhuman

BECAUSE BEING HEALTHY IS SO HOT RIGHT NOW

Now I am the first person to admit that my twenties was jam packed with traveling the world and partying like a ROCK STAR! My health was certainly NOT a priority and it showed. At the age of just 27 I had three surgeries within 18 months;

1. My gall bladder removed
2. My appendix removed
3. Pre-cancerous cells removed from my cervix

Since I was a child, I always had issues with eczema, dermatitis and psoriasis. Not as bad as some of my cousins and aunties but bad enough to have me scratching until I bled and in tears when ointments were put on. Chances are I had some food intolerances that my Mum just didn't know about. Back then the general population and doctors weren't as aware of and educated around food allergies and intolerances like gluten and dairy, so we just lathered the steroid cream on and hoped for the best. As science has evolved, we have come to learn the intrinsic connection between food, body and mind. Our body reads the codes and enzymes present in live foods. It knows what to do with these because Mother Nature designed them especially for our human body's consumption. When we eat highly processed foods it is like our body trying to interpret a foreign language. It doesn't understand or know what to do with these foreign objects. They certainly aren't beneficial to our body's healthy functioning long term. For a lot of people, if you told them they could only ever eat real, raw food from now on they would be struck down by fear and attachment that they could no longer enjoy that _____fill in the blank, chocolate bar, glass of wine, hot chips etc. Ideally what our bodies require are macro nutrients and micro nutrients to function at optimal levels. Macro nutrients include proteins, carbohydrates and fats. Micro nutrients cover vitamins and minerals.

Personally, I'm all about balance, understanding the effects of the foods we eat on our bodies, and making gradual, sustainable upgrades over time. It took a life-threatening experience for me to get serious about my health. It is the same for so many people. If you are reading this book and you haven't yet had a life changing experience to make you lean towards healthy living, I implore you to do so out of the desire to never reach that position. If you decide not to, and risk it for the biscuit, then enjoy your biscuit my friend because life is too short. Hopefully you don't have a life changing catalyst, and if you do, hopefully it isn't a grievous permanent one.

Dr Humbert Smokey Santillo—Health Revolutionary of our time and author of Natural Healing with Herbs, Food Enzymes, Intuitive Healing, Fruits and Vegetables—The Basis Of Health, Herbs Nutrition And Healing

After my time in ICU I started to research different health hacks in an attempt to learn how to upgrade my own immune system the natural way. I've always understood and prioritised the importance of frequent exercise, even just a walk for a minimum of 30 minutes (make sure you commit to nothing less than three times a week) but I wanted more than that. I wanted to commit to creating the most optimal environment for this vehicle of my life, giving it everything it needed to run as smoothly as possible, flooding it with the nutrients it needed to THRIVE. I tried a few different green powders, I even got onto the celery juice fad, but to be totally honest, buying that much celery week in, week out was simply not sustainable for me. Way more grocery bags to carry, storage in my fridge and on a fundamental level, I still always like to come back to balance. Whilst there may be numerous healing benefits associated with celery juice, that main vegetable focus alone is just not balanced. I stumbled across some whole food organics that completely caught my attention. There was a story about a naturopath named Dr Smokey Santillo.

He wrote;

> "I'd like to tell you the personal story that led to the development of this whole-food product. When we're experiencing a trauma or other significant event, we don't always fully understand it until it has passed, and then we realise that it has changed our lives for the better. Living a life is a lesson itself and is always teaching us

135

something; we just have to learn how to interpret the direction it is taking us. Even a chronic illness is pointing us in a specific direction, as I learned when my father got sick.

It was 1980 and I was on a lecture tour, teaching herbal seminars in Denver, Colorado. During a break, I received a phone call from my father. He told me his spleen had swollen to the size of a football. It was so large he was using one of his Marine Corp belts to hold it up and it was so painful that he could hardly move. My mother made an appointment for him at a nearby hospital, where the doctors could not believe how large his spleen had grown—and it was still growing.

At the end of the day, my dad called me again and said he was diagnosed with lymphoma, cancer of the lymphatic system. I was so stunned I couldn't even reply. I just held the phone, praying that I didn't really hear what he had said. My throat closed up, so tight I could hardly breathe. He felt my shock and distress and told me everything was going to be okay. Being a naturopath and teaching people for years how to live by the laws of nature, I had to ask myself, why did this have to happen? (Don't we all wonder why, when something so traumatic happens to us?)

I told my dad I'd be home in four days as soon as my tour was over. By the time I got there, his doctors had already removed his spleen and started chemotherapy. I was floored, totally irate. No questions had been asked—they just did the surgery and started pumping him full of drugs.

After three weeks, my father had lost 40 pounds and nothing was working. The chemotherapy had failed and there was nothing more they could do. His doctor called our family together and told us my dad had no more than three weeks to live. After breaking the news to my dad, I asked if he'd like to try natural therapy at my clinic in Tucson, Arizona, where I would take care of him. He said, "I would have come to you before this, but I didn't want you to be responsible if anything bad would have happened to me." I picked him up and carried him out of the hospital without even checking him out.

By the time we got to Tucson, he weighed 136 pounds, and his cancer was traveling so fast through his body that he couldn't eat or drink. How do you nourish somebody who can't eat or drink? I started massaging him every day with Olive Oil so his body would absorb the fat through his skin. He could only sip water, so I devised a plan to get more nutrients in through another route. I built a slant board for him to lie on, made fresh green juice with kale, parsley and some additional liquid chlorophyll, and used an enema bag to feed him through the bowel with this juice daily.

As he got stronger, he was able to drink vegetable juices by mouth. Fruit juices, however, made him feel ill because of their sugar. You don't want to feed cancer cells sugar, because they thrive on it; plus, it acidifies the body, putting an even greater strain on a sick person's system.

I wanted to find a way to get more concentrated nutrition into his body to increase his strength and boost his healing, and it occurred to me that if I could juice the vegetables and dry the juice, the powder would be more concentrated than the juice itself. I set up some small dryers in my office and found that it would take hours to dry the juice, but it worked. I'd give him table-spoons of vegetable juice powder stirred into small amounts of water daily. To my amaze-ment (keep in mind, at that time we knew nothing about phytochemicals) in two months he put on 30 pounds. There was no meat or carbohydrates other than tablespoons of dried vegetable juice in his diet. I wondered, how could someone put on so much weight without eating?

He then got to the point where he could also drink fruit juice powder without feeling ill, so he'd have fruit juice powder in the morning and vegetable juice powder the rest of the day. I gave him very little fruit juice powder, though, as I noticed that if I gave him too much, his urine's pH would turn acidic. I also added pro-teolytic enzymes and some herbs to the regime. I was constantly changing the dosages of his supplements according to his pH, using the monitoring system in my book, ProMetabolics.

The results were astonishing. Within three months of my taking over his treatment, my father got out of bed and re-modelled my kitchen. He had been a carpenter his whole life and loved working with wood. Continuing with a nutritional program of eating large amounts of vegetables, dried juice powders, and soaked and sprouted seeds and nuts, he went back to work within six months and worked as a carpenter for another six years. It's my opinion that he'd still be alive today if his doctors had not removed his spleen and given him such high doses of drugs during his hospitalisation.

From my father's recovery, I realised the hidden healing power of whole foods, so I began studying all fruits and vegetables known to man, and I learned that some were much more nutrient-dense than others. Ironically, the ones most concentrated in nutrients were the ones most people didn't eat at all, or always cooked before eating parsley, beets, cabbage, and broccoli, to name a few.

Experimenting over several months, I created one concentrated juice-powder formula with fruits and another with vegetables—the most nutrient-dense fruits and vegetables on the planet. Soon my clinic looked more like a produce-drying facility, and everyone who came to me, regardless of the problem, was given a bag of each powder. The healings that I observed were no less than miraculous; I knew I was on to something big when my patients were getting well so fast.

The formulas I used in my clinical practice are now the most wonderful line of fruit and vegetable concentrates. I designed and patented these products, and NSA, LLC in Memphis, and TN manufactured, distributed, and promoted them. Benefiting thousands of people in over 30 countries, these are the most researched nutraceutical in the world today.

Just before my father died, he was so concerned about my professional reputation that he said, "If I die, will people still believe in you? Will they still buy your books?" I said, "Dad, what we accomplished together, this idea of concentrated fruits and vegetables, someday will be known all over the world." And that's exactly what happened. My father's recovery gave birth to the most wonderful product line of fruit and vegetable concentrates.

My father taught me pride and honour. He would tell me that a man's word is all he has. In over 50 years of being a carpenter, he never once had a written contract with anyone—only an agreement of a smile, honour, and love. He will always own a piece of my heart. I know he is always with me; he's my strength and motivation."

WOW! What a story! This took my breath away, one son's love and devotion to help save his father's life. I believe there is no stronger driving force in our universe than love itself. I decided I wanted to find out more about these products and try them for myself. These fruit and vegetable concentrates came in vegan capsules to be consumed daily, flooding the body with a variety of 33 different fruits, berries and vegetables. Our nomadic ancestors used to enjoy an insane amount of variety like this when we lived the simple life, roaming the planet, eating hundreds of different fruits, berries, nuts and vegetables daily, and occasionally sharing some meat between the entire tribe that that had been freshly hunted. There were 38 prestigious medical and scientific journals published demonstrating the healing benefits of these products. This is exactly what I was looking for. A simple, convenient and effective way to up-level my base-line nutrition, every, single day. I was in. Hook, line and sinker.

I received my supply and after a few days had a huge break out on my face. What appeared to be a cluster of blind spots around the corner of my nose. It was causing swelling under my right eye. I couldn't believe these magic beans were giving me acne and swelling my face! I went to the doctors just to make sure everything was ok and was told I had Cellulitis. A common and sometimes painful bacterial skin infection. GREAT. He prescribed me some antibiotics. I try to avoid antibiotics if possible, simply because they kill all the good AND bad cells, taking you down to ground zero. If they are a must, then they are a must. These, however, were NOT a must, and he said that it would eventually go away over time. I left the medical centre without any antibiotics and started researching what was happening to me. It turns out my body was going through a complete detoxification and it was showing up in my largest organ. My skin.

What we have to understand about detoxification is that the body is constantly trying to detoxify itself from substances such as its own dead tissue, cholesterol and uric acid. We live in a world of environmental pollution—everything from toxic chemicals to radiation. Also, we have moved from a nomadic lifestyle of eating 600 hundred different plants—which is still typical for today's rare nomadic societies—to a sedentary life and a diet seriously lacking in that level of variety of plant-life. The body is a miraculous machine and when it is operating optimally, it can repair damaged tissue and cleanse dead material out of the body as well as foreign chemical pollutants. This is done by the numerous biochemical reactions that require a whole plethora of enzymes. However, without the variety of plant matter in the modern diet, for most of us this process of detoxification remains incomplete. This is because with our modern diet, typically we do not get enough vegetables and fruits in our body to adequately nourish all the possible trillions of biochemical reactions that the body wants to engage in to operate optimally.

I understood this was all part of the process and decided I wanted to start including a plant-based protein powder that was jam packed with 20+ super foods—grains, sprouts, spirulina. There was also an epic plant-based omega, NOT getting the omegas from a FISH but instead from the algae that the fish eat and actually PRODUCES the omegas themselves. GENIUS! Within 5 days I noticed a huge surge in my energy. I went from being a bag of bones on the couch at 7.30pm (after the babes' night time routine of dinner, bath, bed, then dinner for my man and me) to having to force myself to go to bed at 10pm knowing the rug rats would be waking me up at 5am. No one appreciates that kind of natural energy at that time of day like a run-down Mamma with a huge workload, let me tell you. If you want to find out more about these epic holistic health activators or even get your hot little hands on some, you know where to go— www.courtneystarchild.com/universe

Rather than cutting things out all together and facing some form of deprivation, I was all about getting educated and making gradual, sustainable, long-term upgrades in my physical, chemical and emotional health choices.

I started researching health hacks and asking myself;

What type of water do you drink?
What oils do you cook with?
Do you eat hormone free meat?
Do you use antiperspirants?
Do you go to sleep after 10pm?
All of these questions helping to educate us of the small changes we can make on a daily basis that have long-term

health benefits. Cutting out unnecessary hormones, using coconut oil instead of vegetable oil, natural deodorants, GOING TO BED EARLY! Gosh! Going to bed early and getting a good night's sleep are so hugely underrated. Do you know we are wired physiologically to cycle with the moon? Ever heard of a circadian rhythm? A circadian rhythm is a roughly 24-hour cycle in the physiological processes (relating to the branch of biology that deals with the normal functions of living organisms and their parts) of living beings, plants, animals, fungi and cyanobacteria. In a strict sense, circadian rhythms are endogenously (having an internal cause or origin) generated, although they can be modulated by external cues such as sunlight and temperature. So why are circadian rhythms so important? Circadian rhythms can influence sleep-wake cycles, hormone release, eating habits and digestion, body temperature and other important, healthy, bodily functions. Biological clocks that run fast or slow can result in disrupted or abnormal circadian rhythms. Being on our screens before bed can impact this natural rhythm. Artificial lighting such as blue light from our phones, tv's and computer screens can impact this natural rhythm. When the sun rises we see blue light telling our brain that it is daytime and helps us to feel awake and ready for the day. When the sun sets and goes dark, the blue and green light disappears and our brain realises its night time. It then secretes melatonin, a sleep hormone that helps us to get sleepy and inevitably fall asleep. Going to bed after 10pm can impact this natural rhythm. Lao Tzu says, "Figure out the rhythm of life and live in harmony with it." He was kind of a big deal. You should really listen to him. You can do yourself a solid and find a Holistic Overhaul Health Hacks Quiz for you at www.courtneystarchild.com/universe so you too can start making these easy little upgrades daily and get yourself humming along your path to your health recovery.

Holistic Human Activation #6

Whole Food Nutrition Support

Fruit and vegetables provide your body with the most important and fundamental phytonutrients; vitamins, minerals and enzymes to help heal itself and optimally function in a harmonious, balanced state. Ideally, they should be consumed every single day. Get educated. Know your stuff. Honour your one lifetime vehicle with supreme gasoline A.K.A wholefoods. Your entire life will benefit BIGTIME! Experts recommend two servings of fruits and five of vegetables every day. For some that is easy to achieve, for others that is not always easy to achieve. Loads of people simply don't have the luxury of time for meal planning or even like the repetition of it, and more often than not the foods are covered in toxic pesticides and then have all of the nutrients cooked out. However you now have this epic health hack to up-level your nutritional baseline, you can easily bridge the gap by supporting your dietary intake everyday with the most researched nutraceutical in the world.

Know this—your body has three main healing systems—the immune system which requires hundreds of thousands of enzymatic symphonies combined from a mix of fruit and vegetables so it can thrive. The digestive system requires prebiotic and probiotic proteins as the epicentre for energy and optimal self healing, while the nervous system requires healthy fats like multiple omegas to regulate and smoothly transport all of the brains messages around the body effectively, improving your mental health. All of these systems require a long term solution. A wholefood plant baseline of fruit, vegetables, omegas, prebiotics, probiotics and protein, teamed with regular exercise. Add in small sustainable long-term upgrades (outlined in The Holistic Overhaul Health Hacks Quiz) and you have got yourself one hellofa powerful combination to get you humming on your journey back to your ultimate happy, healthy immunity strong self! BOOM!

Calm Heart Meditation

Posture

Be in any comfortable position with the spine straight and a light neck lock or jalandhar bandh. Place the left hand on the centre of the chest at the Heart Centre. The palm is flat against the chest, and the fingers are parallel to the ground, pointing to the right.

Eyes

Closed

Mudra

Make Gyan Mudra with the right hand (touch the tip of the index [Jupiter] finger with the tip of the thumb). Raise the right hand up to the right side as if giving a pledge. The palm faces forward, the three fingers not in Gyan Mudra point up.

The elbow is relaxed near the side with the forearm perpendicular to the ground.

Breath

Inhale slowly and deeply through both nostrils. Then suspend the breath in and raise the chest. Retain it as long as possible. Then exhale smoothly, gradually, and completely. When the breath is totally out, lock the breath out for as long as possible.

Concentrate on the flow of the breath. Regulate each bit of the breath consciously.

To End

Inhale and exhale strongly 3 times. Relax.

The home of the subtle force of prana is in the lungs and heart. The left palm is placed at the natural home of prana and creates a deep stillness at that point. The right hand that brings you to action and analysis, is placed in a receptive, relaxed mudra in the position of peace.

Duration

At home try it for 3 minutes. If you have more time, try it for three periods of 3 minutes each, with one-minute rest between them, for a total of 11 minutes. For an advanced practice of concentration and rejuvenation, build the meditation up to 31 minutes.

Scientific Benefits

This posture induces the feeling of calmness. It creates a still point for the prana at the Heart Centre.

Emotionally, this meditation adds clear perception to your relationships with yourself and others. If you are upset at work or in a personal relationship, sit in this meditation for 3 to 15 minutes before deciding how to act. Then act with your full heart.

Physically, this meditation strengthens the lungs and heart.

This meditation is perfect for beginners. It opens awareness of the breath, and it conditions the lungs. When you hold the breath in or out for "as long as possible", you should not gasp or be under strain when you let the breath move again.

Rehash

- ⭐ Get educated about whole food nutrition

- ⭐ Flood your body with whole foods

- ⭐ Allow time for detoxification

- ⭐ Make small sustainable upgrades

- ⭐ Move your body for at least 30 minutes most days

- ⭐ And keep meditating daily

- ⭐ Share your story, journey, experiences, breakdowns and breakthroughs with each other on the Rocking Rock Bottom FB Page

150

HAPPINESS IS THE NEW

RICH

INNER PEACE IS THE NEW

SUCCESS

HEALTH IS THE NEW

WEALTH

KINDNESS IS THE NEW

COOL

WHO KNOWS WHO SAID THAT BUT IT FREAKING ROCKS

CHAPTER 7

Illuminating With Luscious Self Love

WARTS AND ALL BABY... WARTS. AND. ALL.

How funny is it when you grow up and realise that your Mum and Dad are in fact, just regular human beings going about life, doing their best, but ultimately with no better idea about the meaning of life than the next person? And certainly NOT the "know it all" superheroes you believed them to be your whole childhood? (I mean, except for Beyoncé and Jay Z's kids, they are definitely going to grow up with actual superheroes for parents!) I remember the first time I came home from school, asked Mum about some mathematical equation and she responded to my enquiry with, "I don't know." I was in dead shock! My poor little brain scrambling, in slow motion like The Matrix, unable to comprehend the words that just came out of her mouth. "What? What do you mean you don't know? What about that saying—'Who knows, Mum knows' that you have told me MY. WHOLE. LIFE?" The very fabric of my existence coming completely unraveled.

I had always been close with my Mum. We were more like best friends than mother and daughter. We could sit for hours playing cards, talking about life, love, relationships, spirituality. We were both free spirits. I used to love getting deep with her. She would let me go as deep as I could possibly go, so off the beaten track, no topic off limits, and on so many different tangents, even I'd forget what we started talking about. She was always so proud of anything I did, yet I spent a huge portion of my life focused on and striving for the approval and acknowledgement of my father. I remember every night as a little girl when he would put me to bed he would say, "Have I told you today that you are the most beautiful little girl in the world?" I will fondly remember those moments for the rest of my life. However, what stuck with me like glue was a time when I was fourteen years old and I competed in the 800m at the state championships for Little Athletics. From all the weekend comps and personal best times, it was stacking up that I might come in fourth or maybe even jag a bronze if I did a PB (Personal Best). I was so excited. Dad had been training me leading up to the event. By training I mean driving in his car to a point, parking there and timing me run from where he left me to the car. Rinse, repeat. I was also training 4 nights a week, Monday to Thursday at the club. I loved it. Eventually the big day came. State championships. I can still feel the anticipation of that race in my body today. My chest tight, my palms sweaty, a dry mouth, butterflies in my belly. I remember the smell of the track, the hot, dry Western Australian breeze blowing in my face. Mum always told everyone I looked like Flo Jo when I ran. I was so tall it looked like slow motion; one step of mine was equivalent to three of the girls I was racing at the local club.

But today wasn't the local club race. Today was the state championships and all the best of the best competitors from Western Australia were there to compete. We were all allocated our lanes and sent off to the starting line. It was a long wait to settle into our lanes and then silence. "On your marks…….. get set……… BANG!" The gun sounded and we were off, first lap staying in your own lane. I was running as fast as I possibly could, adrenaline pumping through my veins. I loved it. We came to the second and last lap where we could cut into lane one; I made a dash and had a great position in third place. I had my pace on and still had some gas in the tank. We came to the final 200m mark and one of the girls in front of me stepped inside the internal lane barrier twisting her ankle and rolling onto the ground in front of me screaming. We ran past her and across the finish line. I couldn't believe it. I just saw one girl's dreams be crushed, from having a first-place gold medal to disqualified, and there I was getting the silver medal at the state championships! I was so conflicted. So sad for her but so happy that I got a SILVER MEDAL at the state championships! This was not even a consideration in my mind before the race. I was ecstatic! Mum was too. She was wolf whistling like a mad woman! It was such an incredible feeling. After the race I went over to Mum and Dad who both hugged me. Dad said, "With some more training, next year you could get the gold." What's crazy, is that comment totally crushed me. I was so happy with what I had achieved and to my Dad, even that wasn't enough. I was so young and impressionable that this feeling became the undercurrent for the next 15 years of my life. Never feeling good enough, never living up to Dad's expectations and always striving for his approval whilst always unable to attain it.

THE WOUND

is the place

THAT THE

Light

ENTERS YOU

RUMI SAID THAT

When he was 20 he met my mother. She was 21 and separated with two young children to another man. My father was married to another woman who was pregnant with his child. It wasn't a fairytale beginning at all but they fell in love and decided to create a future together. My grandmother on my father's side was not happy with my father's decision to leave his pregnant wife and pick up with my mother, however, my father chose to pursue his own wishes and move forward with my mother. Years later they were living in New Zealand and my mother fell pregnant with me. My sister was nine and my brother was eight. My father told my mother he was going to journey back to Australia indefinitely, by boat, and it was going to take six weeks to get there. With no certainty as to if or when my father might return to his pregnant wife and children, my mother decided to engage the help of a detective friend in New Zealand and find out where my father had gone. She quickly learned he had caught a plane to Sydney and had been there for a few weeks settling in by the time a letter from him arrived in her letterbox detailing his treacherous boat journey there. My mother decided it was his responsibility to look after them seeing as though she was about to have his child and sold everything in their home to buy tickets for her and the children to Australia to come join him.

As the years went by, my father's lies began compounding and becoming more and more blatantly obvious to the people around us. He was a charismatic young guy that liked to tell people stories about how he played rugby for teams he had never played for, how he made four times the amount of money he actually did or how he had investment properties around the world, which he didn't. A traveling salesman he was, having affairs with women all over the countryside. One day my mother received a phone call from a woman who claimed to be having an affair with him. She couldn't believe it. "When did he have the time for that?" she thought.

The woman insisted they meet and so my mother obliged. She had a huge work event on that night where she confronted my father about the affair and as you can imagine, he denied it ever happened. Years of infidelity, more lies, and domestic violence ensued. My brother was about fifteen when he was snooping in our parents' bedroom looking for money. He found a suitcase and opened it up only to find letters from a multitude of women from all over Australia. He didn't know what to do so packed it away and went and told our big sister Sacha. She was the one who broke the news to Mum. Unfortunately, our mother believed that we were better off staying with him rather than packing our bags and leaving him in a blaze of glory. So, we stayed. Two years later my sister had moved out to live with her boyfriend and my brother had escaped away in the night destined for New South Wales. I was the only one left until Mum moved to Bali.

I spent my high school years looking for love in all the wrong places, through my twenties I was a free spirit traveling the world; I was enjoying the freedom of youth and the lack of responsibilities—still looking for love in all the wrong places. My father could never relate to the freedom of lifestyle I experienced as he had multiple children by that age and therefore loads of responsibilities. He liked to tell people that he paid for my travels. It now makes me laugh but it used to ignite a fierce rage in me as it undermined all of the hard work I did, by myself, financially, since both of my parents left me at fifteen, to make my travel dream a reality. At that stage in my life I was still prepared to overlook his lies so we could try to have some kind of relationship, so I moved to Queensland to rebuild my relationship with him. His new wife and I got along famously. She and her five sons will always hold the most special place in my heart, such incredibly wonderful human beings. On occasion she and I would go out to dinner with my father and when the waiter would come over Dad would inevitably launch into one of his stories about "playing rugby for some elite team" or "how much money he makes" she and I would raise our eyebrows at each other and giggle to ourselves. In hindsight it's crazy to think, after all of this, and so much more not disclosed, I spent such a big portion of my life striving for this man's approval. Why? Why did I seek his approval and his acceptance when he couldn't even accept himself and what he had or hadn't achieved in his life? It wasn't until I had my own children in my thirties that I really started to draw a line in the sand between my father and I. It was no longer acceptable to overlook this personality flaw and allow any lies in our lives. I had to be an example to something so much bigger than my desire to have a relationship with my father. I had a responsibility to my very own children. I didn't want to have to explain to them that their grandfather didn't have to tell the truth, although we all did, and we just accepted that about him. I wanted to demonstrate to my children that INTEGRITY was one of our most important values and show them what real self-love looked like. Real self-acceptance. The thing is that was something I now had to go and learn for myself.

162

THREE THINGS
CANNOT BE
LONG HIDDEN

The Sun

The Moon

The Truth

BUDDHA SAID THAT

The moment we look outside of ourselves for approval for anything, we undermine the very essence of self-esteem. The definition of self-esteem is; confidence in one's own worth or abilities; self-respect. That right there is exactly what I want to demonstrate to my boys and for my boys to know deep within themselves unquestionably that they are so very worthy. I recently saw a profound speech by the incredibly soul shaking Lisa Nichols. If you don't know who she is you absolutely need check her out. Such an inspirational woman. She addressed the crowd, asking questions like;

> "Are you willing to disrupt any form of what you know?
>
> Are you willing to re-invent yourself?
>
> Are you willing to become someone you have never seen before?
>
> Are you willing to run, leap and soar?
>
> Even at the possibility that you might fall?
>
> Are you willing?
>
> Are you willing to do something you've never done before?
>
> Say something you've never said before?
>
> Do the things you don't want to do?
>
> Say the things you don't want to say?
>
> So you can be the man, the woman you've always known yourself to be?
>
> Are you willing?"

She then told the crowd of her story, her struggle and she shared;

"See I didn't come here to give you a lot of answers.

I came here to disrupt your soul with a lot of right questions.

Because I wasn't supposed to be here

I was that kid that was always struggling with self-esteem.

Am I good enough?

Am I smart enough?

No one who looks like me makes it anywhere.

I'm chocolate mocha-skin, full lips, round hips and kinky hair

You just don't see me on TV

You don't see me glorified

You don't see me representing beauty

You don't see me

So, the world didn't give me permission to be here

But I didn't ask for it either."

Lisa stepped into her authority and told the crowd;

"So, some of you are still asking for permission

Sometimes you have to stop asking for permission

And it's just time to give the world notice

So, I just showed up to invite you to give the world notice that you are coming

Give the world notice that you have been here

Give the world notice that you have played polite long enough

Now it's time to play full out

Give the world notice that unapologetic just showed up

Give the world notice that non-negotiable just showed up

Give the world notice that if they can't handle your light that you're tired

You're no longer going to dim your light

If they can't handle your light, put on some shades

Because when you become that bold

When you become that audacious

When you become that unapologetic

All of a sudden you become infectious

All of a sudden just the mere glimmer of you

When I can catch a glimpse of you

When I can get in your hemisphere

And your atmosphere and your zip code

Something happens to me

Because I'm in proximity

And then you become absolutely aware

Of the true assignment on your life

That you are here to save us

You are here to inspire us

By the way you walk, with assistance

By the way you rise above your own uncertainty

By the way you push past your religious conversation

Your cultural conversation

Your economic conversation

Your gender conversation

By the way you show up and say

How can I serve humanity?"

She was ELECTRIC! She was hitting every point, pushing every button and getting the crowd uncomfortable enough that they felt compelled to move, to change, to be bold and brazen with their goals and dreams. She asked;

"So, what is your quest?

It might just be to go home and be 1000% present with your children

Your quest might be to love an unlovable sibling

It might be that.

I'm a girl, who as a Mom in 1995

I was broke and broken

And all I was committed to do

Was not spend the next 25 years

In that brokenness

So, I didn't decide my quest out of a pursuit

Of serving the world in a big way

I stepped into my quest

Becoming committed that I won't have it that way anymore

So, however you step, just step

Sometimes you got to step outta something

Before you're stepping into something

Don't get paralysis of the analysis

Trying to make sure the step is right

I'd rather you take ten steps wrong than

Analyze trying to make one step right

One more day

While someone is waiting to be inspired by you

I'm still figuring out how to get it right

But I've done some good work

Trying to figure out how to get it right

One day I'm going to master this thing

One day

So, I just stopped by to stir your soul

I stopped by to not let you off the hook

Of your brilliance, of your genius, of your humanity

Of the willingness to live in constant duality

Allowing your brilliance and confusion to coexist

And you embrace them both

Not waiting for another thing

Not waiting for another person

Not waiting for any permission

Not waiting for someone to validate you

Not waiting for your mother, your father to say you are OK

Not waiting for the man, the woman in your life to say go be free

Not waiting...

What are you waiting for??"

SELF LOVE IS A
CONSCIOUS CHOICE
IT IS THE DAILY
CULTIVATION OF
SELF REFLECTION
ACCEPTANCE
NURTURING
FORGIVENESS
NOURISHMENT
PERSONAL GROWTH
& UNCONDITIONAL

I SAID THAT COZ THATS HOW IT IS FOR ME

It was real. Raw. And potent AF. I loved what she said. Every single bit of it. She rocked that popsicle stand and then some. It's important to remember that it is ok to coexist in the space of "I am awesome" and "Who the hell am I do to this" whilst still forging forward regardless. It's ok to believe what you believe about religion but put those differences aside for the greater good of humankind's inclusive community. It's ok to believe what you believe about sexuality but know that what others choose to do with theirs is their decision and that is where it ends. It's time to stand up and stop waiting for someone else to give you permission to live the life you want to live. That is how I live my life now. I still have moments of seeking validation from outside sources like friends and family and then I have to remind myself to check in and remember that no one need validate me but ME. Once we can truly forgive ourselves, release ourselves of our past, forgive others, release them of their past, our expectations of them, our expectations of ourselves and accept exactly where we are in our journey, only THEN can we truly shine the light from within and give others permission to do the same by leading the way.

Sometimes practising self love is accepting oneself as is.

Sometimes practising self love is accepting your past.

Sometimes practicing self love is forgiving ourselves.

Sometimes practicing self love is forgiving someone else.

Sometimes practising self love is looking in the mirror and saying your affirmations.

Sometimes practising self love is removing yourself from unpleasant situations.

Sometimes practising self love is setting solid boundaries.

Sometimes practising self love is finding a new hobby.

Sometimes practising self love is self care schedules.

Sometimes practising self love is saying NO to things that don't light you up.

Sometimes practising self love is dusting yourself off and trying again tomorrow.

Sometimes practising self love is challenging yourself.

Sometimes practising self love is hard AF.

Sometimes practising self love is nurturing your broken heart.

Sometimes practising self love is committing to your health.

Sometimes practising self love is an all out crying session.

Sometimes practising self love is making the hard decision.

Sometimes practising self love is a long conversation with an old friend.

Sometimes practising self love is filling your cup.

Sometimes practising self love is singing out loud at the traffic lights.

Sometimes practising self love is filling someone else's cup.

Sometimes practising self love is catching up with family.

Sometimes practising self love is a walk on the beach.

Sometimes practising self love is a meditation.

Sometimes practising self love is a kick ass lounge room dance party.

Sometimes practising self love is a kick in the pants to yourself.

Sometimes practising self love is practising self compassion.

Sometimes practising self love is all there is.

Sometimes practising self love is just that. A practise.

And sometimes you just gotta practise.

"Enlightened collectives will fulfill an important function in the arising of the new consciousness. Just as egoic collectives pull you into unconsciousness, and suffering, the enlightened collective can be a vortex for consciousness that will accelerate the planetary shift." That's what what Eckhart Tolle says in his book *A New Earth*. That's what I want to be part of. The Enlightened Collective of Leaders, leading by example, dragging humanity into the vortex of a higher consciousness, a deeper connectedness for all life here on earth. It's time to step up into the SUPERHUMANS we are here to become. Whatever that role is for you. If that is simply being the best friend to your best friend right now. Forgiving yourself or someone else and moving on from that hurt. Creating a loving, happy, safe home for your family—what an epic contribution to the world THAT is! Take that step, be that person and lead from that light. WE ARE THE ONES WE HAVE BEEN WAITING FOR! If you don't deeply love you now, that is OK. Accept where you are at and start working on that. Do your daily affirmations until you transition from trying to convince yourself to deeply believing in yourself. Whether it takes a week, a month, a year, a decade or a lifetime. One step closer to feeling great about yourself everyday is an epic decision to make and take, each and every day. An epic example to lead by. Consciously decide to do the things that make you feel great about being your *unique* self. Engage in those practices. Practise. Practise. Practise. There is no one on the planet or in the universe quite like you, and YOU gotta love YOU baby. Warts and all.

Holistic Human Activation #7

Affirmation Station Illuminating with Luscious Self Love

I invite you now to create two or three affirmations to read to yourself every morning when you wake up, and again before you go to sleep in the evening. You can have these by your bed, stuck on your bathroom mirror for when you are brushing your teeth, in your phone notes, maybe even attached to an alarm? I find it easier when they are in your way so you can see them, engage and continue on with your day without any fuss. A great idea is a whiteboard marker to write on your mirror, it doesn't get in the way and you can update them all the time. Here are three from Louise Hay and a few others that I really like to help you get started;

"I let go of all fear and doubt, and life becomes simple and easy for me."—Louise Hay

"I am grateful for every experience I have ever had as it has shaped me into the person I am today, and that is exactly who I am supposed to be, right this very moment."—Louise Hay

"I choose to make the rest of my life, the best of my life!"—Louise Hay

"My life is a gift. I will use this gift with confidence, joy and exuberance."

"Today I choose me."

"I am worthy."

"I will surround myself with positive people who will help bring the best out in me."

"I release my negative thoughts, embracing positivity and optimism."

"I AM FIERCELY LOVEABLE AND INCREDIBLY WORTHY."—I said that—couldn't you tell?

The Ultimate Healing Activation Meditation

Posture

In any comfortable position, spine straight with a light neck lock

Eyes

Closed

Mudra

Is the most important. The elbows are bent down by the sides and are tucked comfortably but firmly against the ribs. The forearms are almost perpendicular to the floor, with the hands extended out at a 45-degree angle from the centre of the body. Most importantly, the palms are perfectly flat, facing up, hands bent back at the wrists. You should feel a pull in the lowest part of your forearm as you almost hyper-extend your wrist to make the palms flat. (This tends to be the most challenging part of the meditation, so it is important not to let the hands relax out of the position.) The fingers are kept side by side, except that the thumb is spread from the other four fingers.

Mantra

Ra Ma Da Saa, Saa Say So Hung

Ra—Sun

Ma—Moon

Daa—Earth

Saa—Impersonal Infinity

Saa Say—Totality of Infinity

So—Personal sense of merger and identity

Hung—The infinite, vibrating and real.

This mantra taps into the energies of the sun, moon, earth and the Infinite Spirit to bring deep healing. It is important to pull the navel point powerfully on the first *Sa* and on *Hung*. Note that the word *Hung* is not long and drawn out. Rather, it is clipped off forcefully as you pull in the navel. Chant one complete cycle of the entire mantra with each breath. Then deeply inhale and repeat. Remember to move the mouth precisely with each sound. Try to feel the resonance in the mouth and in the sinus area

Mental Focus

You can choose to mentally visualise the person or persons that you are wanting to heal, as you send this energy to them for their well-being.

Duration

Continue chanting for 11 to 31 minutes.

To End

To end the meditation, inhale deeply and hold the breath, as you offer a healing prayer. Visualise the person you wish to heal as being totally healthy, radiant, and strong. See the person completely engulfed in a healing white light and completely healed. Then exhale and inhale deeply again, hold the breath, and offer the same prayer again. Exhale.

To complete, inhale deeply, stretch your arms up high, and vigorously shake out your hands and fingers for several seconds. Keep the arms up and hands shaking as you exhale. Repeat two more times and relax.

Scientific Benefits

In many traditions, healing is said to occur when you raise your vibration into divine alignment. According to the law of attraction, healing must occur if your vibration matches it. This meditation is a way of raising your vibration to the frequency of Divine Healing.

You can find the song to this meditation and a demonstration over at... you guessed it www.courtneystarchild.com/universe

Rehash

- ⭐ Self-Acceptance
- ⭐ Forgiveness for all
- ⭐ Release expectations of everyone
- ⭐ Do more of what makes you feel good
- ⭐ Self-Love Affirmations
- ⭐ Attitude Of Gratitude
- ⭐ MEDITATE
- ⭐ Share your story, journey, experiences, breakdowns and breakthroughs with each other on the Rocking Rock Bottom FB Page

182

DONT DANCE AROUND

The perimeter of the person

YOU WANT TO BE

Dive deeply &

FULLY INTO IT

GABBY BERNSTEIN SAID THAT

CHAPTER 8

Pursuing Your Passion With Purpose

WHITE HOT AND PASSIONATE IS THE ONLY THING TO BE

Your passion can be your hobby OR you can pursue your passion as your profession and never work a day in your life. You really can choose. Now I can already see your eyes rolling in the back of your head thinking, "Yeah right Court, but I still have to pay my bills, put a roof over my head and eat food. That all costs money." I get it, BUT you can start to transition, just one day at a time, one step at a time, one right decision in the right direction AT. A. TIME. Many people work during the day and study at night to transition out of a J.O.B and into a role they are more passionate about, one that fills them up. It may take time to work your way back up to the top starting in a new industry yet, when you are enjoying the "work" you are doing everyday, do you think you will care or do you think you will be busy enjoying your day-to-day life so much more that you won't be fazed if it takes you one year or five or ten for that matter? If you are loving what you do every day? Just let that percolate for a minute. Think about showing up to a place that you love AND doing that thing that sets your soul on fire AND getting paid for it! How freaking RADICAL! Picture it in your mind. Feel it in your heart, your gut, in every cell of your being. Connect TO THAT. Start attracting THAT.

One of my all-time favourite quotes that really sums up this essence of drive for passion in one's life is by Roald Dahl, "I began to realise how important it was to be an enthusiast in life… if you are interested in something, no matter what it is, go at it full steam ahead. Embrace it with both arms, hug it, love it, and above all become passionate about it. Lukewarm is no good. Hot is no good either. White hot and passionate is the only thing to be." This hits the nail on the head for me. There is something so magical and magnetic about a passionate person. My challenge earlier in life was that I was so damn passionate about so many things. How to choose? What I would go back and tell my younger self is "Baby you just need some time, life experience and patience. Enjoy yourself right now. It is all being orchestrated in divine timing and when the time is right, when you slow down, when you settle and truly find where you belong, it will reveal itself. Your true-life path and purpose." And you will be tested along the way, believe me, by your partner, friends, family, bosses, opportunities, everything; just to see how serious and committed you are to what you think you want.

Enabling

BALANCE & BOUNDARIES

In your life

WILL TRULY

Set you free

I SAID THAT - MIC DROP

Whilst I was in recovery from my surgeries and tuning into my higher self every day, I started asking myself what I wanted to do and why. Your personal WHY is one of the most important driving factors in your life, like I have previously said, because it is unique to you and it is super important to figure out so it becomes your true north and your personal compass for your decision making throughout your entire life. When Elon Musk graduated high school, he looked into his future and asked himself, "What do I want my life's work to be?" He decided his life's mission was to "Enable the future of humanity." He has done that so far by introducing PayPal—a way people could pay for goods and services online, and that was a huge break through for online shopping convenience and safety. Now he has moved onto sustainable energy and space travel. WOW. That is pretty amazing and what a powerful perspective to have at such a young age followed by that body of work he has crafted. It is important to keep ourselves in check though and remember, all we ever need to be is better than who we were yesterday. That is the ONLY comparison that needs to be made in our lives, not to someone else's accomplish-ments today, their age and certainly not their social media sizzle reel. Uhhh ahhhh, no way precious soul. You just do you boo, day by day. Looking at your life objectively can help you see what you want to accomplish long term. Your leg-acy. That's it. So when I was sitting in hospital in that dark dense energy, I looked at the people helping those suffering, when no one else was around and everyone was asleep. I sat there watching these magical humans give their lives in selfless service to those who needed monitoring 24/7. It was an honorable act to witness and it triggered that sense of service in myself. I wanted to help people. I had spent many adult years uneducated about myself, my emotions, how to manage them and in suffering, without any consistent pos-itive example or guidance of how to navigate from there. I turned to drugs and alcohol as an escape and thought it was loads of fun at the time. I looked back and thought, what might have helped me back then? What might help these people sitting here in hospital beds contemplating life, their health, and possibly their death? Some perspective, some practical tools to use from right there in those beds, the very things I had to go through and experience to unveil these exact Holistic Human Activations in this here book. It was a bittersweet twist of fate, but isn't that what all of life's lessons are about? They are here to push us, to make us so uncomfortable that we have to move, that we have to WAKE UP and charge fiercely after the things that matter most, the things that set our soul on fire! I thought about writing this book and beyond that I started to question my strengths. I know I am a creative soul who loves art, storytelling, live events, helping people, personal development, skating, interior decorating, live music, yoga, meditation, sound healing, snowboarding, the list goes on. How was this going to serve humanity? I started to think about what I was naturally good at. In multiple jobs throughout my career I had always performed well teaching, story-telling or presenting. I started to think about this book and how I could help as many people as possible, out of suffering and into supreme joy just by practising these things, and then one day it came to me, during deep meditation;

A live event (which I loved) CHECK

Story telling (which I loved) CHECK

Live Music (which I loved) CHECK

Personal Development (which I loved) CHECK

Helping People (which I loved) CHECK

Motivating People (which I loved) CHECK

Meditation and Sound Healing (which I loved) CHECK

Sharing tools from experts to help people out of suffering (which I loved) CHECK

THIS WAS IT! And so, the idea of a Live Activation Event was born. I was lit up when I came out of that meditation. I was having full-blown downloads, my heart was racing, I was so excited, so passionate, so in alignment and so on purpose. THIS GIRL IS ON FIIIRRREEEE!! I could barely contain myself and got to work on each of the subject content categories: Business, Mind, Body and Soul. Later that month I took my babes down to the magical Tallebudgera Creek just near our house to have a swim and a run around. As they were playing at the park a lovely woman came past and said, "Two boys, you are my hero." We shared a smile and a laugh as she walked off after her one little fella. As our kids started to play together on the playground, we were standing near enough to talk to one another when she mentioned, "My girlfriend has just had twins." "Oh, they aren't twins," I replied, "there is a fifteen-month age gap, but the young fella is massive." We laughed again and I noticed her accent. She was a Kiwi. Hold on a minute, I knew a woman I previously worked with, years before who had recently had twins and was also a Kiwi. I proceeded to ask if it was the same woman, turns out it was, and they were best friends who had moved from New Zealand to Australia together many moons ago. What a "co-incidence". I asked what she did for work. She was an event coordinator. "Funny that, I might just need an event coordinator seeing as I'm about to put together an event." How crazy. Now what is even crazier is that months before this, one of my closest girlfriends told me about this super down to earth Mamma Bear on Instagram and YouTube that she thought I had to follow. I checked out this awesome Mamma, loved her vibe and started following her on Instagram. I had only started getting into Instagram a few months earlier (very late adopter but hey, that's me) so my bestie, Amanda was always giving me tips and telling me about fun people to follow and how to work this app. Then when I was "downloading" all these ideas about The Self-Empowerment Movement during my meditation, I thought this Mamma Bear might just be the perfect fit to speak at the event about Self-Empowerment by pursuing your Passion With Purpose. The lady in the park continued to tell me about her new business and that she had just booked a national tour for an Instagram Mumma and asked if I had heard of her. Turns out it was the same Mamma Bear I had been looking to approach. I couldn't believe it, but then again, I could totally believe it. It was only a few weeks later when I was getting my lashes done and I was talking to my lash babe about my event and going through the process of reaching out to speakers when she said, "My girlfriend does that kind of thing and would be a great match. Have you heard of her? Turns out it was the same Mamma Bear again. That was it. I had to reach out and get this woman on board. It was destiny.

The reason I tell you this long-winded line of coincidences is because at this point, I was so emotionally attached to this woman and this story that there was no way this collaboration wasn't going to happen. One thing I had made very clear from the beginning of the inception of this idea was: if it doesn't align and flow, it's not a go. I used to be all about hustle, now it was different. Now I was about living in alignment with my destiny and what the universe had in store for me, not what I thought it had in store for me. This can be a really difficult dance sometimes as there is a fine line between determination and pushing in the wrong direction, surrender and giving up. All I can tell you is this, if you sit down, tune into your situation or circumstance, the feelings that arise will trigger your physiological response. This should either make you feel elevated and in alignment (because expansiveness is our natural state) OR pushing against forces far greater than yourself, swimming upstream or contraction (and then surrender and a pivot in another direction is best). It might be tough but true, so you are best to just roll up your sleeves (Thanks Meg Mac) and get on with things to avoid getting emotionally bogged down in that place. After reaching out, giving my number, speaking directly to this wonderful woman and booking her in as a speaker—two weeks later she ended up retracting her agreement to honour herself not overcommitting and I was left feeling devastated. I spiraled out of emotional control to that place, you know the one we all default to;

"What the hell am I trying to do here?"

"I'm not even an event manager."

"Who would want to come to my event?"

"Who would want to read my book?"

"I'm not going to do this event."

"I'm not cut out for this kind of rejection."

Blah blah blah..

And so on. It's REAL. Those debilitating thoughts come and go in every single human's mind from time to time. The key here is acceptance and release. See and feel these experiences as just that, experiences, like the four seasons of the year. They come and go, so it is extremely important for us not to unpack in that place and stay, but instead feel the feelings, thank them for their lessons, let go and move on. Give your new tapping tool a spin? This one took me one whole day to get over. I reached out to my bestie; she sent me a list of other babes she followed on Instagram and told me to keep on going. They are exactly the kind of friends you want to have in your life. No judgment, purely there to help bounce you back to being on track when you need it most. I realised I had romanticised this story of all these coincidences and attached to this one person. Hindsight the next day

194

reminded me, this event was not about her; yes there were some amazing coincidences, but this right now was not in alignment. This right here was a clear demonstration of the universe testing me to see how much I really wanted to create this event. Had I thrown the towel in with this one hiccup I would have demonstrated to the universe that this was not what I was truly setting out to achieve. What was required here was supreme surrender and a pivot in the right direction. And so, I went on... as I do... and so can you sweet cheeks.

I believe passionately in what it is I am trying to create right now and although The Self Empowerment Movement didn't come to pass when I had originally planned for it, I still feel passionately about the why behind my purpose and truly believe that sometimes you simply need to surrender your plan to the universe in exchange for something bigger and better that it has in store for you. Often far greater than what you had in mind to begin with. Now, what I want to do with my life and what you want to do with your life could be very similar or very different. It doesn't matter. We all have our own path with our own unique spin. If you just focus on being one percent better each day, in 100 days time you will be 100% better, not to mention the compounding effect of this becoming more rapid over time. Your job is to get yourself happy and grateful for the life you have moving in the right direction towards the future you want. There really are no rules in this crazy thing we call life.

NONE.

Now YOU just need to take ownership, get very specific and get busy designing it. Its go time baby!

WE ARE THE
Music Makers
WE ARE THE
Dreamers Of Dreams

WILLY WONKA SAID THAT

So how do you go about taking this kind of affirmative action towards creating this dream life of YOURS and pursuing your passion with purpose? You create your very own Universal Energetic Emotional Signature. To do that you write out a list of specifics that you desire for your life, for example lets think about a checklist for your dream job;

I want to work from a co-working space

I want to make X amount or more annually

I want holidays where and when I desire

I want to be my own boss

I want to LOVE what I do

I want a low stress role

I want to be creative

Then write out all the feelings you will experience whilst living this dream life.

Attach an image, letter or animal to this. Put it somewhere you will see everyday. Then as you go about your day-to-day life, each time this letter, object or animal appears, your job is to invoke the feelings you will feel whilst living this life in present tense, sending out an emotional signature to the universe, placing your order for this life, attracting the same emotions you send out repeatedly, every single day.

Look at your life objectively, so you are consciously aware of the important things you want to achieve long term, break them down into bite size pieces and turn those bite size pieces into small right decisions in the right direction for your day-to-day life. Now I want to make this very clear, I'm not talking about micro managing your life, I'm talking about breaking down what it is you want, focus on one main thing at a time, tuning into those feelings, those emotions, looking at the things you want to achieve long term and putting the milestone goals down on paper so you can set yourself some realistic expectations. BUT REMEMBER—divine timing is always at play so whilst you might decide you want to have a new house by "X" date, you also need to have the emotional detachment to the timeline. Surrender to the universe knowing that what you want may come to you in a way and a time you had never imagined before. Understand your emotional state attracts situations and people equivalent to that. Envisage yours and put together a practical plan because if you fail to plan you plan to fail. Then go ahead and get started. At the end of all of those continual right decisions you will find those super important BIG things you want to achieve unfold right there before your eyes and then VOILA, one day you wake up and reflect to see you are, in fact, living the life of your dreams baby. REAL LIFE = DREAM LIFE. You planned for this. You are the entrepreneur responsible for designing your life. Take some responsibility. Organize that sh** right here right now.

Let's get cracking already, whoop whoop!

Holistic Human Activation #8

Epic Emotion Attraction Plan

I'm sure most of you have heard of "The jar of life — Rocks, Pebbles, and Sand" story. If you have not, here is a quick refresher. The original story: A philosophy professor once stood before his class with a large empty jar. He filled the jar with large rocks and asked his students if the jar was full. The students said that yes, the jar was full. He then added small pebbles to the jar and asked again, "Is the jar full now?" The students agreed that the jar was indeed full. The professor then poured sand into the jar and asked again. The students then agreed that the jar was finally full. The professor went on to explain that the jar signifies one's life.

The rocks are equivalent to the most important things in your life, such as family, health, and relationships. And if the pebbles and the sand were lost, the jar would still be full, and your life would still have a meaning.

The pebbles represent the other things that matter in your life, such as your work, school, and house. These things often come and go and are not permanent or essential to your overall well-being.

And finally, **the sand represents the remaining small stuff and material possessions in your**

life. These things don't mean much to your life as a whole and are likely only done to waste time or get small tasks accomplished.

The metaphor here is that if you start with putting sand into the jar, you will not have room for rocks or pebbles. This holds true for the things you let into your life too. If you spend all of your time on the small and insignificant things, you will run out of room for the things that are actually important. So, **in order to have a more effective life, you should prioritise important things in your life and then worry about pebbles and sand at a later time.**

Think of the rocks as your desires, set out clearly the things that are important to you, the things you want to have in your life. Next write out all of the elevated emotions associated with this outcome. These are your pebbles; the things that make you feel good and activities that ignite those feelings in you. Then you can get really specific, return to your Introverted Excavator Self Enquiry and work backwards from what you wrote down. What do you love? What do you want to achieve? What are the small but significant steps you need to take towards this each day? Here is an example of breaking it down. When I decided I wanted to write a book (DESIRE) there is some preparation I needed to take. Working backwards. Questions I needed to ask myself to give me the direction I need to craft this milestone or "ROCK".

How many pages will my book have? How many chapters? What topics will they cover? When do I want this completed by? How many pages will I need to write each week to achieve this? Once you have broken down each goal or dream then apply your S.M.A.R.T. Guidelines to each one and break them down from long-term actions to short term and map out the trajectory of your dream life. PS. My book took way longer to write than I had anticipated but I surrendered to the fact that there was more I needed to experience before she was ready to come to completion. That universe... she is always so right.

- **S**pecific
- **M**easurable
- **A**ttainable
- **R**ewarding
- **T**ime Bound

Write these out so you have a step by step, bite size piece map, of how to get to where you want to go BUT consciously decide that you are emotionally detached from the finer details like timeline and how because life isn't perfect, sh** does happen, and in such a poetic way that we cannot even explain, so you need to embrace the times of change, pivot when things don't feel in alignment with your intuition, rejoice in the spontaneity, relish in the synchronicity of serendipity and live in the balance between your projected plan and the universe's divinely timed plan for you. Sometimes that is easier said than done but you catch my drift and you will get better at surrender as the years go by, I know it. Remember to add your Universal Energetic Emotional Signature to each of your S.M.A.R.T goals and focus on one at a time..

You can head over to www.courtneystarchild.com/universe for a download printable option to do this activity.

Breath Of Fire

Posture

In any comfortable position with the spine straight

Eyes

Closed and focused at third eye point

Mudra

Hands can be rested on your knees

Breath

Breath of Fire is one of the most powerful pranayama in history. It is rapid, rhythmic, and continuous. It is equal on the inhale and the exhale, with no pause between them (approximately 2-3 cycles per second). It is always practised through the nostrils with the mouth closed, unless stated otherwise.

Breath of Fire is powered from the navel point and solar plexus. To exhale, the air is expelled powerfully through the nose, by pressing the navel point and solar plexus back toward the spine. This feels automatic if you contract the diaphragm rapidly.

To inhale, the upper abdominal muscles relax, the diaphragm extends down, and the breath seems to come in as part of relaxation rather than through effort. The chest stays relaxed and slightly lifted throughout the breathing cycle. When done correctly, there should be no rigidity of hands, feet, face, or abdomen.

Duration

Begin practising Breath of Fire for a duration of 1—3 minutes. Some people find it easy to do Breath of Fire for a full 10 minutes right away. Others find that the breath creates an initial dizziness or giddiness. If this happens, take a break. Do not practise while pregnant or on your menstruation cycle.

If this explanation is too confusing you can easily head over to www.courtneystarchild.com/universe for demonstrations.

Scientific Benefits

- Releases toxins and deposits from the lungs, mucous lining, blood vessels and other cells.
- Expands the lung capacity
- Increases Vital Strength
- Strengthens nervous system to resist stress
- Repairs balance between the sympathetic and para-sympathetic nervous systems
- Strengthens naval chakra
- Increases physical endurance
- Adjusts subtle psycho-electromagnetic field
- Reduces addictive impulses for drugs, smoking, bad foods
- Increases oxygen delivery to the brain, facilitating a focused neutral mind
- Boosts the immune system to help fight disease
- Promotes synchronisation of the biorhythms of the body's systems

Rehash

- ✪ Identify Your Passions

- ✪ Am I feeling expansive or contracted?

- ✪ Know Your True North

- ✪ Acknowledge The Seasons of Life

- ✪ Surrender And Pivot

- ✪ Universal Energetic Emotional Signature

- ✪ You guessed it... MEDITATE

- ✪ Share your story, journey, experiences, breakdowns and breakthroughs with each other on the Rocking Rock Bottom FB Page

Passion fuels THE ROCKET While vision GUIDES IT TO ITS Ultimate Destination

OBVIOUSLY AN AWESOME HUMAN SAID THAT

CHAPTER 9

Attaining Wild Abundance

HAVING AND BEING MORE THAN YOU HAVE EVER IMAGINED POSSIBLE

In a time where we have more than ever before, the majority of the population will tell you they could still have more, need more, want more and certainly earn more. Crazy isn't it? "The average wage in Australia is $78,832 according to The Australian Bureau of Statistics. If you plug that into www.globalrichlist.com it shows that you are in the top 0.28 percent of the richest people in the world by income. Even on the average Australian wage you're richer than 99.72% of the global population," says Scott Pape, one of Australia's most famous and influential financial advisors. Isn't it just absurd that you don't think you are ABSOLUTELY loaded right now? You really do have everything you already need and it's time to make a huge shift of perspective about this. Not just for your head space but also to enhance your Universal Energetic Emotional Signature for unlimited abundance. After my parents' separation we didn't have a lot of money. Mum went to work for a furniture company and wasn't home until late each night leaving me to come home to an empty house at thirteen years old. I was a pretty well-behaved kid I must admit. Usually a bunch of my friends and I would whip up a batch of pancakes for afternoon tea and call up the local radio station requesting songs. That was all the rage back then, sometimes even make some prank phone calls for the hell of it but that was about as naughty as we got. It wasn't long in her unfulfilling furniture sales career that Mum found out that the Parental Support Payments from the government worked out to be very little difference com- paratively from her take home pay, so she decided to quit her job and be home for me. Those were the years I loved most as we used to sit around talking, just the two of us or sometimes with friends, playing cards and listening to all time classics like Jimi Hendrix, Bob Marley, Smokey Robinson, Eurhythmics, Michael Jackson, Roachford and The Forest Gump Soundtrack. Those albums instantly take me back to those days. Each week Mum would give me a ten-dol- lar allowance for the weekend, and I would head out with my friends for some fun. When she moved to Bali and Dad to Queensland, I started to receive Living Away From Home Allowance and Rental Assistance from the government. To me, at fifteen, I was now rich! I paid my rent and food money to Carmel, my Dad's ex fiancé whom I was now living with and had about fifty dollars left over. Five times what I used to previously get. What a pay rise. That meant I could go and buy a new item of clothing each week if I wanted to and still have money left over for the weekend, which was a huge deal to me back then. Although I had this new stream of income, I was still heart broken, missing my Mum, crying to my stepsister Carly whom I shared a room with. Lucky for me she was the most loving and affectionate human that I have ever met on this Earth, still to this day. I would lie there on the bottom bunk bed listening to The Cranberries while I quietly wept, trying not to disturb anyone else in the house. She would hear me cry and climb down from her bunk and just cuddle me, for hours. I couldn't have picked a more loving and accepting family to be adopted into. Still to this day I have a close loving relationship with every member of this family including Carly's big brothers Ryan, Anton and their father Jonny. After the thrill of "new things" wore off and missing my Mum really settled in, I learned one of the most valuable lessons of a lifetime. Happiness far surpasses any material objects and certainly money. I learned to manage money at a very young age and prioritise what was important to me. The non-negotiables like rent and food were always paid first, then the rest was spent on having fun with my friends. Like I said before, during my final two years of school all I wanted to do was travel. When I finished school and eventually moved to Sydney I started to save to go and do that travel and continue to focus my money on the things that lit me up and brought me happiness like inexplicable cultural experiences around the world.

212

TO ACCOMPLISH
Great Things
WE MUST NOT
Only act
BUT ALSO DREAM
Not only plan
BUT ALSO BELIEVE

KILLER QUOTE BUT WHO KNOWS WHO SAID THAT, SORRY NOT SORRY

After returning home from travel, eventually meeting Josh, falling pregnant, moving to Queensland from Sydney and coming out of the work force, I realised I had gone from this absolutely free spirited and independent woman to the complete opposite end of the spectrum and was now a dependent, sleep deprived, Ground Hog Day, stay at home Mamma. This was such an incredibly difficult transitional time for me. I loved my children and loved being a mother, as I do now, but this was a full-blown identity crisis zone. I fell pregnant with Cassius when Hendrix was only five months old and both babes went ten days overdue, so of a twenty-three-month period I was pregnant for twenty months. I had never felt like such a recluse from the rest of the world and so dependent on someone else. The level of vulnerability was enormous. That's when Josh started his new hobby, hunting, going away every few weekends, leaving me with our two new babes and that's when my real personal development journey began. Feeling extremely vulnerable and alone, like many new mothers nowadays do, with the vast majority of my friends interstate. I was very blessed to have Mum around the corner for the extra support. I realised that I looked to Josh for so much more than what he was able to give me emotionally in those times and I had to learn to relinquish him from my expectations of what I thought he should be doing. Finances had changed from our double income and only two mouths to feed, to a single income and four mouths to feed. We spent as he earned and lived week to week for many years until a wake-up call meeting with our accountant to discover we had in fact been going backwards for a while now. We needed to make some big changes and the time to start was NOW.

I had heard some people like Anton—my stepbrother, Marnie—my best friend and Aaron my big brother—some of THE most important people in my life—talk about this book called The Barefoot Investor. I decided it was time to read this book and take on these changes so Josh and I could reclaim our financial security, independence and freedom. When I was in my twenties and saving to travel, I had my bank accounts set up so I had multiple linked accounts, one for expenses, another for savings and another for fun. When I read The Barefoot Investor, I chuckled to see that my own set up in my twenties hadn't been too different from what this expert financial advisor Scott Pape was educating thousands of Australians to do. Monique Bowley from MamaMia.com.au described Scott Pape's following as "The Biggest Financial Cult In Australia." Here's how she put it

As I pulled my bankcard out of my wallet and scanned the PayPass the cashier gave me a smile.

"You're one of them," she said

I nodded back, slightly embarrassed.

My cult status was exposed. "I'm on it to," she confided. "And I see it almost every day."

Right now, thousands of Australians are flashing orange bankcards with mantras penned on with sharpies and stickers. 'Splurge' they read, 'Daily Expenses,' read others.

And they all signal one thing, that you are following the biggest finance cult in Australia.

One of the biggest take-aways in the book is about having multiple "honey pots" for your money. Most people only have one. Money goes in to that one account, money goes out of that one account or "honey pot". Emergencies pop up and even more money goes out. Scott explains with incredible simplicity some easy fundamentals to help you take charge of your current financial situation without having to be on a backbreaking budget day in and day out. Some of his hot tips are:

- Fee FREE bank accounts
- Get a great Online Saver Account separate from your everyday access account
- Get great insurance
- Roll over all of your Superannuation into one account
- Three "honey pots" for your hard-earned money
- Live off 60% of your income—save the rest for fun and freedom

I want to make it very clear I get no benefits from sending you to The Barefoot Investor book, I'm just here to share with you fine folks the tools that empowered me along the way and this one was an absolute GAME CHANGER! It was simple and I loved it. By now you know *I LOVE* simple. Anybody could do it, young independent guys, young independent gals, single Mammas, single Pappas, Grand Mammas, Grand Pappas, anyone and everyone you know. How liberating would it feel to cut up those credit cards that have been holding you hostage for years? We could all have a plan that helped us to live handsomely as some of the richest people in the world. And above all else, what I loved about this man's work is he understood the importance of the vibrational emotional frequency of having savings. If your emotional relationship with money is strenuous, hard to come by, scary, scarce and fearful, the vibration you send out around this will match that, and money will continue to be exactly that for you—strenuous, hard to come by, scary, scarce and fearful. If you have some savings in your account, typically you feel safe, secure and happier about life—you therefore attract more of the same. Wayne Dyer said, "Abundance is not something we acquire, it is something we tune into". I trust you have been practising your meditations for some time now so you will know exactly what he is talking about when he refers to the abundance you tune into right? You need to start to take accountability for where you currently sit financially, and know that, with many little right actions, many little right decisions, day by day, you can better this situation and create a financially secure lifestyle for you and your loved ones with those family holidays or girls/guys trips away that you may have only ever dreamed of before. Once again, if you fail to plan you plan to fail. Don't do that. Put a line in the sand right here, right now and say enough is enough. I can do this. Get yourself a copy of The Barefoot Investor, make the changes you need to make, do the work you need to do and in only a matter of time you will set yourself financially FREE. Cue song "Shackles" by Mary Mary.

"Cut the shackles off my feet so I can dance. I just want to praise you; I just want to praise you."

Raise your hands, dance and rejoice in the fact you are going to be financially FREE for life!

That is certainly something to sing and dance about so get excited baby, oh and be grateful too!

Holistic Human Activation #9

Sweet Money "Honey Pot" Plan

If you want to take full advantage of this epic advice—this epic tool of empowerment to create your very own "Sweet Money Honey Pot Plan", then you are going to have to buy another book... you guessed it. The Barefoot Investor. Sorry not sorry. Scott details exactly how he rebuilt his family's financial situation after their house was burned down in a fire and like I outlined above, it is so simple. It is a plan anyone can start today and follow. Make the plan. Stick to the plan. Deliver the life of your dreams. STAT. It doesn't need to be difficult; it doesn't need to be about deprivation. It needs to be about balance, boundaries, the bigger picture and commitment. You can change your ways now and dramatically change your future. In the famous lyrics by The Killers "Change your ways while you're young" and if you're not young anymore, just change your ways, you deserve to be secure and happy, now and forever. It will happen a lot faster and more pain free than you currently believe, you just have to get started by making one right decision at a time. You know the drill.

Metamorphosis With
The Magic Mantra

Sit

In any comfortable position with the spine straight

Eyes

Closed and looking down at your hands through your closed eyes

Mudra

Lift your hands to the level of your heart, palms up, elbows relaxed by your sides. Form a shallow cup of your hands by placing the sides of your hands together from the base of the palms to the tips of the Mercury fingers (pinkies). All the fingers are together but not rigid. Open the thumbs out away from the hands. The cup is not deep, the edges of the cup are about thirty degrees up from the parallel plane.

It is important to keep the "line of Mercury" connected; the outsides of the hands touch from the Mercury fingers to the base of the palms. Normally there will be no opening what-ever, but some people will have a gap between their little fingers. Keep this gap to a minimum.

Mantra

Chant Ek Ong Kar Sat Gur Prasad along to the song. This means God and we are one, I know this by the grace of the true guru, that god and we are one. Whatever god is to you. The Creator, ruler of the universe, the supreme being, Spirit, whoever or whatever god is to you, you and god are one. Guru means from darkness to light. You can find a great version of this mantra as a song along with my demonstration at www.courtneystarchild.com/universe and get lost in the mantra as you practise. This is a wild way to get into a trance like state for ultimate healing to take place within your one time human life vessel.

Duration

In your own time work up from 5 minutes to 11 minutes then the whole 21-minute version of the song. You will absolutely adore the effects you experience practising this powerful mantra. Chanted for prosperity. It is usually chanted in reverse (Ek Ong Kar, Sat Gur Prasad, Sat Gur Prasad, Ek Ong Kar). Many pages are devoted to the explanation of this mantra and we are warned to chant it in reverence. It means "There is one Creator".

Scientific Benefits

This is a gutka shabd—one that reverses the mind. It is the essence of the Siri Guru. If the mantra is chanted just five times it will put it into reverse. It is so strong that it elevates the self beyond duality and establishes the flow of spirit. This mantra makes the mind so powerful it removes all obstacles. Its positive effects happen quickly and last a long time. This mantra brings great intuition to the practitioner.

Rehash

 Acknowledge your current relationship with money

 Reset to ensure a positive perspective & vibration

 Read The Barefoot Investor Book

 Make your Money 'Honey Pot Plan'

 Stick To Your Plan

 FINALLY book and take those holidays you deserve

 Share your story, journey, experiences, breakdowns and breakthroughs with each other on the Rocking Rock Bottom FB Page

222

Abundance

IS NOT SOMETHING WE

Aquire

IT IS SOMETHING WE

Tune into

CHAPTER 10

Helping Humankind Shine Bright Like A Diamond

DON'T DIM TO FIT IN—STAND TALL AND BE SEEN

Since the beginning of time The Human Race has had an intrinsic desire to be part of something more, something bigger than themselves, a tribe or community. After all, together we do make up the largest living organism, encapsulated by the ozone layer and suspended on the backdrop of infinity so it kind of makes sense that this desire is woven deep into our DNA. We crave loyalty, protection and camaraderie that we find in the people we choose to surround ourselves with, which is why it is so very important on a totally primal and instinctive level. It not only determines who we are as individuals, but how we live and interact with the world around us.

The importance of finding your tribe should NOT be under-estimated. A tribe creates an environment for sharing ideas whilst also promoting a sense of community and caring for one another, which is vital for a healthy, productive, fulfilling life. These groups can provide a fundamental sense of purpose and connection, a deeper reason to interact with each other and even provide many physical, emotional and spiritual wellbeing benefits. History.com tells of an unprecedented DNA study that found evidence of a single human migration out of Africa and confirmed that Aboriginal Australians are in fact the world's oldest civilisation. Their customs are the oldest in the world and one of those fundamental ancient customs is storytelling. Aborigines, First Nations, Inuit, and Metis cultures have long passed on knowledge from generation to generation through oral traditions. Storytelling is a traditional method used to teach about cultural beliefs, values, customs, rituals, history, practices, relationships, and ways of life. It tells people who they are, where they have come from and what it took to get them there whilst creating a true sense of belonging for all members of the tribe. Brene Brown says, "We're wired for story. There's a surprisingly simple reason why we want to own our stories of struggle. We do this because we feel the most alive when we're connecting with others and being brave with our stories." The idea that we're "wired for story" is more than a catchy phrase. Neuro-economist Dr Paul Zak has found that following a story—a narrative with a beginning, middle, and end—causes our brains to release cortisol and oxytocin—often referred to as our natural "happy hormones". This causes you to feel a surge of positive energy and these chemicals trigger the uniquely human ability to connect, empathise, and make meaning. Storytelling is literally in our DNA.

Another ancient tradition from our world's oldest civilisation is Sound Healing. The Aborigines have long used the powers of sound which is not just a new age phenomenon but extends back thousands of years into the ancient times where mystical instruments of all kinds were used to remedy illnesses and revive the spirit. From the Aboriginal use of the yidaki (or didgeridoo) to heal physical ailments, to the ancient oriental use of the gong for spiritual attunement, music therapy has been used in many cultures and traditions for thousands and thousands of years for a reason.

So how can the use of sound healing benefit you?

Well, sound is a vibration, and as we already know all of life exists at its core as vibrating atoms. Depending on the instrument, we can be influenced on a cellular level by the vibrations transmitted. Some instruments in particular help us to move from what are known as "Beta Brain Wave Patterns", or those associated with concentration, anxiety and flight or fight reflexes, to calmer frequencies known as "Alpha", "Theta" and even "Delta" brain waves. These brain waves are associated with relaxation (Alpha), meditation (Theta) and trance like states (Delta).

So, what does this mean?

This means that you can access more reviving, rejuvenating and serene states of mind and healing simply by listening to, or learning to play, certain musical instruments. This in turn promotes:

- More mental, emotional and physical balance

- Reduced stress and anxiety
- Improved concentration and memory
- Improved sleep
- Enhanced immunity
- Greater creativity
- Heightened spirituality
- Enhanced spiritual healing

In truth, sound healing is another affordable and easily accessible form of healing you can experiment with that does not require you to consciously do anything except receive. It will invoke your innate healing systems and enhance your life on so many levels beyond your conscious comprehension. If you would like to receive some free sound healing from me, you can jump over to www.courtneystarchild.com/universe and tune in anytime of the day, any day of the month, 365 days a year. From my heart to yours.

230

Into the wild
i GO
To lose
MY MiND &
Find my soul

For my birthday in 2019, rather than enjoy a lavish dinner and drinks with friends and family as usual, I decided I wanted to start the year feeling fresh and aligned so I headed to a sound healing retreat hosted by my personal sound healing mentor, Bebe at Mount Warning in Queensland. Before my throat surgeries I had attended one of her sound healing evenings and absolutely loved it. After my stint in hospital, I reached out to Bebe again and booked myself in for a one on one healing session. Throughout the session I was feeling loads of heat and tingling at the incision site of my new scar. After the session I was completely blissed out and at peace. Bebe told me my guides had come to say that I had not been listening to them and it was time to step into my power, share my gift and share my story. She invited me to lead a guided meditation at her upcoming workshop and I happily obliged. This marked the return to my teaching meditation and sound healing workshops. Six months later was the retreat she was hosting. I had been teaching my own monthly workshops since then, seeing Bebe weekly for group sessions, practising my own craft, healing myself and healing others. In the shower before I left for Mount Warning I burst into tears. I was nervous and sad. Sad because I was choosing to spend my birthday with a bunch of strangers and NOT my babies, AND nervous because it was my first time doing a juice fast, and I don't know about you, but one thing I know about me is that if I don't eat, I get HANGRY! (Hungry + Angry = HANGRY) On the drive I had been feeling quite anxious and it was getting dark. I was running later than expected, I couldn't see where I was going, and the GPS signal was dropping out of range. I started turning on myself. The internal dialogue went something like this...

"You're a silly woman, you have a terrible sense of direction."

"I can see the headlines now, Mother Lost In A Forest."

"Can't even make it to a retreat on time."

"Why did you even come away from your boys for this?"

And so on. Are these the kind of words my water vessel wants spoken over it to form crystals? I think not! I finally arrived and then like a headless chicken was wandering around this campground, no idea where I was and no idea where I was going or where the tribe were. I called Bebe. She came out to find me and led me to the incredible space she had created. Dim lights, the smell of essential oils diffusing, calm warm souls filling the room, soft music, it was aesthetically nurturing on all levels. I chose a mat and sat down.

Shortly after we began, an Indigenous Australian gentleman came to join us with his didgeridoo. He explained the importance of spiritually grounding ourselves before we meditate so we can fly to the highest heights. I have spent many years meditating, done Vipassana which is a 10-day silent meditation and completed a 1000 consecutive day Bound Lotus meditation practice, with many other variations along the way, so you might say I have had a few different experiences with meditation over the years. However, one thing I had never experienced before was visions. My meditation practice had always taken me to a place of vibrational connection with all things. Ideas and pictures maybe, but nothing more (is there even more than that?) and certainly nothing less. So, as we laid down and closed our eyes, this gentleman began to play his didgeridoo. I experienced a deep, solid, heavy comfort of the ultimate grounding. The sound reverberating inside my ear, I could have sworn the gentleman had picked up his instrument and placed it right next to me, playing there for me exclusively, no one else. The vibrations of the didgeridoo telling the story of his elders as they got to work clearing the energies that had been keeping my frequency low for so long. As the energies released, I came to see the beginning of all time. It was complete darkness in the desert. The tribesmen were dancing around a fire lighting up the earth just around them, the didgeridoo played and like sonar the sound waves warned them of approaching predators in the night. The sound of the instrument was low and deep creating a true sense of primitive belonging. As my essence danced with the sound, our rhythm became one and I slowly took form into the life of a huge, powerful eagle. As I gained more strength, each pulsation from the vibration timed with each inhale as I grew the span of my wings becoming greater and greater until I was able to take flight. I went up into the sky and circled around the tribe, protecting them from their predators of the night. It was insane! I could taste the red dirt in my throat, the sound of the didgeridoo penetrating my very existence and then WAAADUPPPP!! The didgeridoo sound suddenly ceased, and I was instantly returned to ashes on the ground from which I had initially emerged.

WOW.

Never in my life had I experienced anything quite like this. So pure and so natural. As if it was woven deep in my ancestral DNA. I felt ALIVE......CONNECTED. Part of something so much bigger than just me. And one thing was for sure, I knew I wanted to keep having experiences like this and help others around the world to have them too. That deep sense of connection, belonging, knowing. Everyone needed to experience THAT!

236

OUR DEEPEST FEAR IS NOT

THAT WE ARE *inadequate*

OUR DEEPEST FEAR IS

THAT WE ARE *powerful*

BEYOND MEASURE

IT IS OUR LIGHT NOT OUR *darkness*

THAT MOST FRIGHTENS US

YOUR PLAYING SMALL DOES NOT SERVE THE WORLD

THERE IS NOTHING *enlightened*

ABOUT SHRINKING SO OTHER PEOPLE WONT FEEL

INSECURE AROUND YOU

KEEP ON SHINING MY FRIENDS

AS WE ARE LIBERATED FROM OUR OWN FEAR OUR PRESCENCE

Automatically liberates others

MARIANNE WILLIAMS SAID THAT

Unfortunately, in our modern world we have become so disconnected from our tribe and become so increasingly **I**-solated with our **I**-phones as we further develop our **I**-ndependence. We no longer feel the need to ask any favours of our next-door neighbours as we have corner stores everywhere with any other convenience at the tap of a button on our phones. We no longer ask for directions or the time as we have those answers and don't NEED anyone else. We know our people are out there—somewhere, anywhere—but we are distracted and disconnected from them. We subconsciously seek them, we scroll past them, but seldom do we make the time to reach out and have those long, deep conversations further nourishing our soul, deepening our connection. We are so caught up in our busy individual worlds that we forget the soul satisfying bliss of prioritising time with the ones we love, the ones who live far away, the ones who lift us up, and inevitably we wind up feeling distanced, depressed, spiritually disconnected and even rundown and sick.

Im pretty sure it was one of my "Sheroes" again, Brene Brown who told a story about a village where all the women washed clothes together down by the river. When they all got washing machines, there was a sudden outbreak of depression and no one could figure out why. It wasn't the washing machines in and of themselves. It was the absence of time spent doing things together. It was the absence of community. In this modern Western world, individualism has begun to reign supreme. The goal of so many is to be an individual who marches to the beat of their own drum unrestrained by others. Individuals who prefer community are often looked at with suspicion, but what if our quest for individualism and independence is actually what is contributing to making us miserable and sick in the first place? Isolated and alone? I personally believe this is what has bought our society to its knees. To the brink of complete depression and anxiety, which is in fact a poetic twist of fate, because as we know, if we AREN'T uncomfortable we don't MOVE. So for the epic evolution of consciousness we have become so independent and isolated that we now need to come full circle and realise it is time to return to the ways of old. Time to return to our tribe. What if belonging to a tight-knit group that requires loyalty and self-sacrifice, love and dependence is THE key to feeling fulfilled in our modern day lives?

As we each weave our intricate life story, the average human traverses numerous tribes as societal, emotional and cultural needs develop. From family to workplace and everything in between, the multi-faceted influences upon a person's life are what make them unique. Finding your tribe gives you a sense of belonging and you will know it innately, your soul will sing as you resume your place within your tribe.

I am so blessed to have experienced this innate wisdom in many places I have travelled around the world and been apart of multiple tribes along the way. My school buddies whom I still see on travel escapades around the country, my Sydney Crew who often come to visit me on The Goldie, My Mutha Sistaz in Canada who love from afar and now My Girl Gang on the Gold Coast. If you have ever moved, interstate or overseas, you know all too well what that feels like. It can be really tough and people can be really "cliquey", so the thing to remember is this, if you can't seem to find a tribe of people YOU click with, think about the things that you love, art, reading, surfing, snowboarding, whatever it is, jump online and look for groups already out there. Join them. If you can't find one, maybe it is time to be brave and bold and go out and make your very own. People everywhere are yearning for connection with like-minded souls and your initiative could become the single greatest decision you have made in your life to date, potentially saving the lives of others just like you by simply creating a space for you all to belong and connect together.

My Perth Tribe

My Sydney Tribe

My Canada Tribe

My Gold Coast Tribe

The change of the times is offically here my people! "The Aquarian Age is upon us. There have been many Ages and shifts of Ages before in the long history of Humankind, but THIS shift of Age is different. The old Piscean Age was dominated by machines and hierarchy, the Aquarian Age is ruled by AWARENESS, INFORMATION & ENERGY. The greatest power will be your word—your consciously projected words. This change is radical, not incremental. It is a simultaneous change in both the outer and inner worlds. The mind is changing its sensitivity, its basic frequency and functioning. Our lifestyle is changing its sense of time, space, relatedness and relevancy. Accept your wholeness and connectedness to a larger creative existence and express it with each committed action. Let your actions demonstrate wisdom. Real value will come from truth embodied in practical actions and in the internal caliber and qualities of your mind and heart. This is the profile of a fulfilled human being."—Yogi Bhajan said that.

244

THE 5 KEYS FOR THE AQUARIAN AGE

1) Recognise the other person is you

2) THERE IS A WAY THROUGH EVERY BLOCK

3) When the time is on, start & the pressure will be off

4) UNDERSTAND THROUGH COMPASSION
OR YOU WILL MISUNDERSTAND THE TIMES

5) Vibrate the cosmos the cosmos shall clear the path

YOGI BHAJAN SAID THAT... TOTAL LEGEND RIGHT?

Have you noticed the changes going on around you? Obviously COVID-19 has had a huge impact on the Human Species and Our Planet Earth at large, but before sh** got crazy with COVID did you notice the people already starting coming together? The protests, the demonstrations, the activists, the youth of today raising their hands, raising their consciousness, raising their voices, stepping up to be seen, caring about our planet because there is NO PLANET B! Caring about their bodies because you only get ONE! It is time for us to change, as a collective, consciously, not just the minority, the MAJORITY. I truly believe COVID is part of the master plan. We need to create the vortex and RAISE THE OTHERS UP! Meditation is no longer a taboo and should be common practice for the masses, men, women and children alike to save ourselves from suffering. But not one size fits all. Whatever it is that meditation looks like for you. That moment of complete connectedness, be it deep-sea diving, bush hiking, staring your baby in the eyes. WHATEVER MAKES YOU FEEL CONNECTED. That is the key. That is YOUR form of meditation. It doesn't need to be rigid and it certainly doesn't have to be traditional or any one of the activations I demonstrate and share in this book. It is completely unique to you. You choose. You will know. Stilling the mind long enough to receive the gift of connectedness. THAT is what it is all about. Figure out what that is for you and practise it as often as possible. As you grow, it may change so bend with the wind, don't break. Step outside of your comfort zone and try new things, experience new things. GROW.

An unnamed Hopi Elder from The Hopi Nation, Oraibi, Arizona said, "There is a river flowing now very fast. It is so great and swift that there are those who will be afraid. They will try to hold on to the shore. They will feel they are torn apart and will suffer greatly. Know the river has its destination. The elders say we must let go of the shore, push off into the middle of the river, keep our eyes open and our heads above water.

And I say, see who is in there with you and celebrate. At this time in history we are to take nothing personally, least of all ourselves. For the moment that we do, our spiritual growth and journey has come to a halt. The time for the lone wolf is over. Gather yourselves! Banish the word 'struggle' from your attitude and vocabulary. All that we do now must be done in a sacred manner and in celebration. We are the ones we have been waiting for."

Same message, different tribe. It is time to come together as a full-blown Connected Earth Collective.

And so

THE NEW WORLD

Was born

250

Holistic Human Activation #10

Humming Bee Breath
AKA Your very own built in
Sound Healing Tool!

Sound Healing is an effective and proven modality that uses vibrational sound to help reduce stress, alter consciousness and create a deep sense of peace, well being and better health. Sound has also been shown to be a vital part of our healing process following illness, injury or surgical intervention.

A fundamental principle of sound healing is that our body supports an underlying energy field, which generates symptoms of emotional, physical and mental behaviours; if we change the energy field we change the resulting behaviours. Equally every part of our body displays synchronistic frequencies, if part of our body is out of sync with the rest that part may become, or already be, diseased. Sound has the capacity to synchronise our body frequency. "Continued and sustained harmonies fed into a field of disharmony will harmonise the field". Correcting and rebalancing our body frequencies empowers wellness.

Certain frequencies are very healing for the human body and when two systems are oscillating at different frequencies there is an impelling force called resonance that causes the two to transfer energy from one to another. When two similarly tuned systems vibrate at different frequencies there is another aspect of this energy transfer called entrainment. Entrainment causes those systems to align and to vibrate at the same frequency.

Because Sound does not appear solid in nature but expresses as vibration, it has the ability to carry right into our cells and even rearrange our molecules. Correct sound frequencies can enhance the resonant frequency of our body, restoring balance, health and harmony to our physical, emotional, mental and spiritual selves. Sound Healing is totally non invasive, there is no touch, no ingestion or no injection involved.

Optimum wellness results when we are vibrating in harmony at our natural and inherent resonant frequency. When one of the resonant frequencies of our body begins to vibrate out of sync dis-ease or ill health occurs. When this happens, an imbalanced sound pattern or vibration has been established within one or more levels of our being. Sound Healing can help us to restore the inherent vibration via sympathetic resonance.

Sound Healing works through entrainment, which is a law of physics. Entrainment occurs when two or more oscillating bodies lock into phase so that they vibrate in harmony with one another. This law of physics also applies to other more complex structures such as the brain. Brain wave entrainment relates to the brain's actual electrical resonance to rhythmic sensory stimulation, such as pulses of sound or light. When the brain receives stimulus either through the eyes, ears or any other of our senses, it emits an electrical charge, a cortical evoked response. If the brain receives a repeating stimulus, it responds by synchronising these electric cycles to the same rhythm. This is called Frequency Following Response, or, FFR.

FFR is used in sound healing to stimulate special brainwave frequencies that are associated with positive well-being. As brainwaves are intimately related to mental states of consciousness, by creating sounds associated with brainwaves that lead to peace, calm and healing, we bring about positive changes. FFR is also linked to the creation of deep spiritual states including deep meditation, lucid dreaming and moments of realisation. An example of this can be found when working with 4-8Hz, Theta brainwave frequency. Theta is associated with both sleep and deep meditative states. Working with 4-8 Hz sound pattern is extremely helpful in manifesting the sleep/meditative state and can be used as a basis for any Sound Healing delivery for any person suffering from insomnia, stress, tension and general anxiety.

"Since the human body is over seventy percent water and since sound travels five times more efficiently through water than through air, sound frequency stimulation directly into the body is a highly efficient means for total body stimulation, especially at the cellular level. Direct stimulation of living cellular tissue using sound frequency vibration has shown marked cellular metabolism and therefore a possible mobilisation of a cellular healing response". Jeffrey Thompson, Director of the Centre for Neuro-acoustic Research, California Institute for Human Science.Speakers/Performers

Humming Bee Breath

Sit

Or lay down in any comfortable position with the spine straight

Eyes

Closed and focused at the third eye point.

Mudra

Lift your hands to cover your eyes whilst using your thumbs to block each of your ears.

Breath

Simply inhale through the nose, a nice long inhale and hum a nice long hum on the exhale, inhale and hum on the exhale. Continue.

Duration

As long as you like.

Scientific Benefits

Bhramari is a safe, easy-to-learn practice, has tremendous therapeutic potential. Like other pranayamas, its power comes partly from its effects on the autonomic nervous system (ANS). Lengthening the exhalation relative to the inhalation activates the calming parasympathetic branch of the ANS. For those who suffer from anxiety or anxious (*rajasic*) depression, the practice can begin to quiet the mind within a few breaths. The noise of bhramari's incessant buzzing can drown out the endless mental tape loops that can fuel emotional suffering, at least for a few minutes, making it a useful starting point for those whose minds are too "busy" to meditate.

256

Rehash

So, what can you do to help humankind shine bright like a diamond?

I'm so glad you asked sweet soul...

You can start by healing yourself first.

Practise going gang busters on gratitude... Every. Single. Day.

Exercise the potent power of now by choosing love over fear everytime you get stuck.

Conquer your badass consciousness by educating yourself on your emotions and training your triggered response.

Have crystal clear certainty with conviction who you are and what you stand for.

Rock your story like a rockstar and let your mess become your message.

Harmonise your health by getting educated about food and supporting your one lifetime vehicle.

Illuminate with luscious self love by accepting yourself, forgiving all & releasing all expectations.

Pursue your passion through purpose and master the art of surrender & pivoting accordingly.

Attain wild abundance adopting a positive perspective and activating your "honey pot plan".

And through this process you will help all of humankind shine bright like a diamond.

You have more knowledge, strength and capability to achieve your wildest dreams than you know.

You just need to begin.

One day at a time.

One step at a time.

One small right decision at a time.

THE END
What All Good Things Must Come To...

Was it as good for you as it was for me?

As I conclude my first book I am overcome with such a huge sense of joy, gratitude and love for you my readers, "My Rockers." Going on to rock your rock bottom. Thank you from the bottom of my heart for supporting this little hype girl from Perth, working hard towards making her big dreams come true to help heal humankind. I never dreamed that I would write a book. Then when I did, I didn't believe I could finish it. Sixteen months later, now that I have done just that, I can't believe my own eyes. I am so grateful for the opportunity to share my story with you. My hope for this book is that these tools help to inspire you into action, encourage you to overcome adversity and empower you out from your very own "rock bottom" and into the happiest, healthiest most holistic version of yourself that you have ever dreamed possible. I am by no means a Guru, and these methods are not new nor original to me, but epic, ancient, proven and powerful practices I have learned along the way to share and help raise the collective consciousness. I hope you have found here within some tools of transformation to experiment with that lead you to create a reality beyond your wildest dreams. I hope you learn how to heal yourself from the hurt, how to truly triumph over your trauma, to indeed harmonize your health and above all else illuminate with luscious self love... because we all know you cant truly love someone else until you truly love yourself! I can't wait to meet you, really see you, really hear you, hold that space for you, share the tears with you, rejoice the triumphs with you and close it all out with one hell of an almighty high five! You've got this. I know you do. I believe in you. So until then my "Rockers" go kick some cosmic ass!

With deep soul gratitude, an ocean of love, ever lasting light & a dash of darkness,

Courtney xoxo

Life is to become
SUBTLE ENOUGH
To hear your
SOUL
& strong enough
TO DO WHAT IT SAYS